CW01081578

'TWENTY BY FOURTEEN'
A History of the South Wales Tinplate Industry 1700-1961

'Twenty by Fourteen'

A History of the
South Wales Tinplate Industry
1700-1961

Paul Jenkins

GOMER

First Impression—October 1995

© Paul Jenkins

ISBN 1 85902 203 0

Printed in Wales by Gomer Press, Llandysul, Dyfed.

This book would not have been written were it not for
God's Inspiration, Love's Labours.

It is dedicated to all those who have been associated
with the tinplate industry in South Wales.

I am deeply indebted to British Steel-Tinplate
for supporting the publication of this book.

All royalties will be donated to help sick children in South Wales,
especially those who enter the Paediatric Surgical Unit of the
University Hospital, Cardiff for treatment.

CONTENTS

INTRODUCTION

> In Britain the inhabitants of a promontory called Balerium are
> particularly friendly to strangers and have become civilised through
> contact with traders from foreign parts . . . They prepare the tin,
> working the ground in which it is produced very carefully . . . They
> beat the metal into masses shaped like astralgi (knuckle bones).[1]

This observation of what is thought to be the Celtic inhabitants of
Cornwall was noted by Diodorus Siculus, a Greek traveller and writer,
in the first century BC. An early reference to the availability of tin in
Cornwall in this chronicle of the Welsh tinplate industry is not without
significance as the proximity of the Cornish tin reserves to the mineral
resources (ironstone and coal) of South Wales was fundamental to the
industry's concentration in an area extending from Llechryd (Dyfed)
in the west through to Lydney (West Gloucestershire) in the east, with
Ebbw Vale as the northern-most point. Of course, many other factors,
to a greater or lesser degree, were to have an influence on the establishment of the industry in the region around 1700 and its subsequent
expansion. The phenomenal pace and scale of the industry's expansion
here soon gained South Wales undisputed acknowledgement as the
premier tinplate producing region in the world—a position it held for
almost two centuries. Just why this should have happened will be
examined later; first it is necessary to have an understanding of the
properties of tin and the uses made of them by man.

Tin is a metal that needs to be transformed from its mineral state,
i.e. tin ore, by the process of smelting before it can be used to good
effect. Invariably, tin-bearing ores are associated with granite rocks or
the sedimentation resulting from their erosion. The only ore of
economic significance is cassiterite which, in its purest form, has a tin
content in excess of 78 percent. Cassiterite is usually found either in
thin, often irregular veins or lodes within the primary rock or, as the
product of the erosion of the primary rock, in alluvial deposits in river
beds and valleys.

The properties of tin—malleability, low melting point, softness,
corrosion resistance, non-toxicity—and the uses to which they can be
applied have long been appreciated and exploited by man. Of the
many applications for tin the most significant are:

(a) as an additive to other metals to produce alloys (bronze, white metal, babbit, pewter) with improved properties to those inherent in the base metal.

(b) for solder, by which two metals can be joined together without adversely affecting their conductivity.

(c) for coating more perishable metals thereby enhancing both the durability (i.e. inhibiting the natural tarnishing and destruction processes) and the appearance of the base metal.

Archaeological evidence suggests that the potential of tin was first appreciated by man some 5,000 years ago. Later civilisations discovered that copper, if mixed with tin (usually in the ratio of nine parts copper to one part tin) whilst the former is in the molten state, acquired the qualities of hardness and tenacity whilst retaining much of its formability. This alloy, known as bronze, was used to manufacture weapons for hunting and warfare, domestic utensils and articles of personal adornment. Credit is usually ascribed to the Sumerians, the inhabitants of Mesopotamia (the area of land situated between the Rivers Tigress and Euphrates) during the period 3500 B.C. to 2500 B.C., for advancing man's knowledge of metal working to a level of capability that enabled bronze to be manufactured.[2]

The tin ore smelted by the Sumerians and other early cultures was extracted from small surface deposits scatted throughout Europe and Asia Minor. Later improvements in mining techniques, although primitive by modern standards, facilitated the exploitation of the more extensive sub-surface deposits of Spain and of Bohemia and Saxony. In Britain, the mining and smelting of tin was one of the initial metal working activities and the tin obtained from the smelted ores figured prominently in the establishment of Britain's earliest trading relationships. The British reserves of tin bearing ores were (and still are) unique to Cornwall where the mining and smelting of tin on a fairly continuous basis was initiated by the Celtic inhabitants of the area sometime between 1000 B.C. and 600 B.C., i.e. in the late Bronze Age. Increased exploitation of the Cornish tin reserves raised Britain's status as a tin producer and exporter to a premier position during the period beginning with the exhaustion of the mines of Northern Spain in the mid-third century A.D. and continuing through to the late twelfth/early thirteenth century when increased levels of extraction from the massive tin deposits of Bohemia and Saxony reduced the tin consumers dependency on the British resources.[3]

But even after the exploitation of the Central European tin reserves the British tin mining and smelting industry continued to have a major influence upon world trade in the metal until well into the eighteenth century. Tradition has it that the Phoenicians were the first of many overseas traders to exploit the Cornish tin reserves and this is given a measure of authenticity by Herodotus, who died around 414 B.C., informing us that: 'the Greeks knew the Phoenicians obtained their tin from Britain'.[4] Irrespective of who it was that first established a trading relationship with the Celtic tin workers of Cornwall they must have been impressed, as were those who followed them, by the purity and abundance of the indigenous tin deposits. Testimonies to the qualities of Cornish tin are numerous and include that penned in 1497 by an anonymous Italian who said of Britain: 'This island produces a quantity of iron and silver, and an infinity of lead and tin, the latter which is of the purest quality'.[5] Also impressed was Giacomo Soranzo, a sixteenth century Venetian traveller for in a report on England made to the Venetian senate in 1554 he stated: 'In Cornwall they have . . . tin mines from which they extract metal in great quantity, and of such good quality that the like is not found elsewhere'.[6] Further confirmation of the excellence of Cornish tin can be found in the 'Pirotechnica' written by the expert mid-sixteenth century technologist, Vanoccio Biringuccio. In his statement, Biringuccio says of Cornish tin: 'According to what I have heard from experienced men, the best and most abundant that is found in the provinces of Europe is that which is mined in England'.[7]

The use of tin in society prior to the medieval period was not confined to its combination with copper to produce bronze. An equally important early application was the manufacture of pewter—a composition best described as 'almost pure tin'. Contemporary pewter consists of 92% tin—a level of purity matching that of 22 carat gold (87.5% gold) or sterling silver with a 92.5% silver content. Modern society generally regards objects made of pewter as ornamental (and not particularly fashionable at present) rather than practical, whereas in the past they were essential features of the domestic scene, comparable perhaps with contemporary plastic-ware. It would appear from the evidence available that before the Roman period knowledge of pewter manufacture was confined to a few Mediterranean civilisations. The earliest pewter artefact surviving today dates from the Egyptian eighteenth dynasty i.e. around 1500 B.C. Later, the use of pewter-ware spread throughout Europe mainly as a consequence of

11

the expansionism of Rome, the Emperor's troops taking pewter articles with them on their campaigns of subjugation. Several hoards of Roman pewter have been unearthed in Britain, including objects such as large plates and dishes (some up to 15" in diameter), pedestal bowls, flagons and brooches.

Easily cast when in a molten state into moulds to give the required shape, pewter provided a relatively inexpensive means of manufacturing household articles. The casting process was made easier and the end product harder by the addition of other metals—notably lead—to the molten tin in various but altogether small quantities. The judgement of the pewterer in mixing the ingredients to produce a quality of pewter that best suited the required article was of paramount importance, so much so that pewter manufacture became a guilded craft in Britain.

Because of its high lead content (often as much as 20% or 30%), pewter is nowadays regarded as a totally unsuitable medium for the manufacture of fluid carrying vessels or food utensils. High lead content pewter also has a tendency to blacken with age creating a rather unsightly product. As a consequence of this somewhat undesirable condition, the pewterers' guild concerned itself throughout the Middle Ages with bringing about a reduction in the level of the lead inclusion. Evidence for this can be found in the 1348 English Statute requiring 'Fine Pewter' to be made with as much brass 'clothes', i.e. copper, as the metal would take with 'Vessels of Tin' being manufactured with no more than 26 pounds of lead to every 112 pounds of tin (i.e. a 19% lead content).

In most European countries a distinction was made between the 'Fine Pewter', which was pewter hardened with copper, and 'Common Pewter', containing some 10% to 20% of lead.[8] For many centuries pewter rivalled wood as the principal medium from which household utensils were manufactured but from the fourteenth century onwards the importance of both was challenged by a new material—tinned iron ware—produced by applying a coating of tin to articles previously fashioned out of iron to give a hard-wearing but attractive finish. The use of tin in this manner seems to have originated simply as a consequence of the manufacturer's desire to improve the aesthetic qualities of otherwise lacklustre bronze and iron articles.

The method of tinning used in the pre-Roman period required the metal worker to simply rub a stick of solidified tin over the heated surface of the article to be tinned in the presence of a suitable flux, the adhesion occurring as a consequence of the tin melting when coming into contact with the hot surface of the base metal. Initially, only copper and bronze articles were coated with tin but soon objects made out of iron—a harder and more durable metal—were being treated in this way. From the fourteenth century onwards tin has been used increasingly for coating ferrous metals, inhibiting to a considerable degree the natural tarnishing and rusting processes. Today, approximately 40% of world tin production is utilised in this way reflecting the importance of 'tinned plate', i.e. a thin sheet of steel coated with tin, to modern society. Tinplate is used primarily for the preservation of food and beverages with lesser quantities being applied to the manufacture of paint and oil cans, aerosol containers, reflectors, electronic equipment, toys and battery shells. But it is in the familiar form of the can of beans, peas, beer etc. that tinplate has become an important, some may claim essential, feature of contemporary life.

Undoubtedly, the escalating demand for tinplate since the First World War is directly related to the expansion and diversity of the food canning industry. The widespread availability of canned foods has contributed substantially to the achievement of higher living standards amongst the populations of not only the Developed World but also, if to a lesser but nonetheless important degree, of the Third World territories. As Professor W.E. Minchinton has commented: 'As an expendable packaging for food and other products, tinplate has been an important agent in the social revolution of the twentieth century by which the variety of diet has been increased and the labour of food preparation diminished'.[9] A visit to the local supermarket certainly confirms modern society's dependence on the tin can.

Finally in this introductory section, a comment on the origins of the word tin. Unquestionably,. similarities exist between the English word and those used to denote the metal in certain European languages, especially the German 'zinn' and the Swedish 'tenn'. It is not difficult to discern the relationship between the French 'etain', the Italian 'stagno' and Spanish 'estano', all closely resembling the Cornish 'sten', the Gaelic 'stan', Manx 'stainey' and Welsh 'ystaen'.[10] It is interesting to note the similarity in word styles between countries having a strong Celtic influence, possibly reflecting the early importance of the Cornish tin trade. As little evidence exists to support this view, it must remain no more than romantic conjecture.

NOTES

[1] *Historia Naturalis,* Vol. V.

[2] Hedges, E.S., *Tin in Social and Economic History* (Edward Arnold Ltd., London, 1964).

[3] Barton, D.B., *A History of Tin Mining and Smelting in Cornwall* (D. Bradford Barton Ltd., 1967).

[4] Hatcher, J., *English Tin Production and Trade Before 1550* (Clarendon Press, Oxford, 1973).

[5] Ibid.

[6] Ibid.

[7] Ibid.

[8] Hedges, E.S., op. cit.

[9] Minchinton, W., *The British Tinplate Industry: A History* (Oxford University Press, 1964).

[10] Hedges, E.S., op. cit.

1. 'TO BEGIN AT THE BEGINNING'

Whatever you wish to tin over in iron, file first, and before you touch it with the hand, throw it in the pot of melted tin with grease and stir it with tongs until it becomes white.[1]

This description of the early method of tinning, i.e. the application of a coating of tin to manufactured articles, was written by a monk, Theophilus Rugerus, in the first half of the eleventh century. The technique described is simple, requiring only a very basic knowledge of metallurgy. The procedure began with the reconstitution of refined and solidified tin into a molten state within a crucible heated by means of a fire positioned underneath. Using a pair of tongs to hold the articles, the tinner dipped them one-by-one into the pot of molten tin, an occasional stir being given to ensure an even and consistent covering. When thoroughly coated, each article was removed from and held over the pot for a few moments to allow any excess tin to run off before being hung up to dry. Within a short while the tin coating hardened, rendering the article ready for use.

When or by whom it was first realised that a coating of tin would enhance the appearance and durability of copper, bronze or iron-ware is not known. The evidence available suggests that the art of tinning has been practised in Britain for over a thousand years and probably even longer on the European mainland. The use of iron as the base metal gradually gained in significance over both copper and bronze mainly because iron-stone—the mineral from which iron is obtained through the process of smelting—was more readily available than copper ores. Equally as important is the fact that iron, having greater strength than bronze, was better suited to the manufacture of weapons and domestic utensils for which durability was an essential quality.

Unfortunately, it cannot be established beyond all reasonable doubt that the tinning of iron-ware was a skill practised in Wales during this early period. Certainly, tin coated iron artefacts dating from medieval times have been unearthed in Wales but these may well have been manufactured outside the Principality and brought in during the period when the Norman influence was paramount. By coincidence, an interesting find associated with this period was tin coated iron keys discovered in 1947 during the site preparation work for the construction of the iron and steelmaking complex at Port Talbot, West Glamorgan.[2] The keys were examined by experts at the National Museum of Wales in Cardiff, who dated them to the thirteenth century.

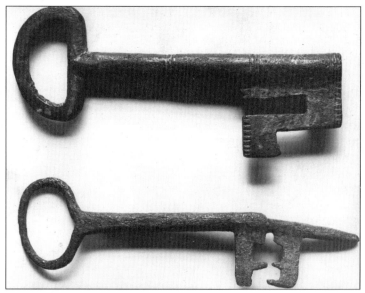

Tin coated iron keys dating from the thirteenth century discovered during excavation work at Margam Moors in 1947 prior to the construction of the Abbey Works of The Steel Company of Wales Ltd. (now the Port Talbot Works of British Steel Strip Products).

It can be assumed from both Theophilus's comments and archaeological discoveries that the initial method of tinning involved articles being given a coating of tin after having been fashioned into their final form; the essential characteristic of tinplate, or more accurately 'tinned plate', is that the iron (or steel from the late nineteenth century onwards) base is coated with tin whilst in a flat form and only after tinning is the article worked into its final shape.

The earliest years of the 'tinned plate' industry are still shrouded in obscurity; its beginning cannot be attributed to any single event or particular individual. Documentary evidence of the emergence of the industry is scarce but that which exists suggests that the manufacture of tinplate evolved in the German province of Bavaria during the course of the fourteenth century. The elements required to make tinned plates in essence are a source of tin and a supply of iron sheets onto which the tin can be deposited. It is known that the exploitation of the tin reserves of the Erzegebirge Mountains began around the year 1240;

it is also recorded that in 1270 a forge capable of producing a flat iron sheet was operating in the Upper Palatinate region and that by the year 1340 production at the forge had reached a level that surpassed local demand. Surplus-to-requirement iron sheets were therefore available for export to other German provinces.

Given the existence of these conditions, it is conceivable that the combination of the two principal elements necessary for the manufacture of 'tinned plate' occurred around the year 1340, possibly at Wunsiedel in Bavaria. Although developing slowly at first, fifteenth century financial support from the German tin merchants encouraged those associated with the embryo industry to extend their activities into new territories, notably the Nurnberg and Amberg regions of the Upper Palatinate.

Further sponsorship during the early part of the sixteenth century influenced tinplate makers to move eastwards into Saxony, the region which remained the centre of tinplate manufacture until well into the seventeenth century by which time an export trade in tinplate with other European countries had long been established by the German manufacturers.[3] Again, documentary evidence of this trade is fragmentary but it is likely that the German merchants regarded Britain, or more precisely England, as an important source of demand for their tinplates. Port records for the period 1618-19 indicate that 9,400 single sheets and 20,000 double sheets of tinplate were imported through London to meet the needs of the tinsmiths whose trade—the making of articles such as basters, kettles, pots, ovens, pans, boxes and basins from tinplate—had been established in Britain before the end of the fifteenth century.[4]

Stimulated by the 1599 Act of Common Council which called upon all householders to: 'cause to be hang'd without their door a substantial lanthorn' (i.e. a lantern usually made of tinplate), activity amongst the tinsmiths increased significantly.[5] As the domestic market for tinplate goods expanded so did the need for a steadily increasing supply of tinned plate. It was as a result of this increased demand from the tinsmiths, generally concentrated in an area of London called 'Crooked Lane' (hence the term 'Crooked Lane Ware' for early tinplate articles), that a British tinplate industry was founded—an event of significant industrial and social consequence for South Wales.

The outbreak in 1618 of the Thirty Years War involving the German

States disrupted the supply of tinplate from its traditional and well-established base centred on Dresden where under the patronage of the Duke of Saxony the trade 'supported five or six brave Cities'.[6] As the quantity of tinplate available for export from the German manufacturers declined so competition between the European importers intensified causing a dramatic and hefty increase in price. The consequence of these supply and financial constraints was that tinplate importers sought to establish manufacturing facilities of their own in order to guarantee their source of supply and thereby weaken their dependency on the German tinplate-makers. Manufacturers in France, Sweden and the Spanish Netherlands all endeavoured to break the German monopoly.[7] Likewise in Britain, several attempts were made to establish a domestic industry with that of John Tilte of London and Bromsgrove being worthy of particular note. Whilst there may have been other and perhaps earlier efforts, his was the first recorded British experience in manufacturing tinplate.

Documents originated by Tilte that have survived the passage of time confirm the experiments. On the 12th September 1623 he wrote to his uncle seeking further financial assistance for the venture and in the letter stated:

> Upon good consideration hereof my neighbour and partner (in this business) we have upon a trial wrought up one ton of iron and have made as good plate as any that comes from beyond the seas. We can tin them ourselves. By this trial we find that good profits will by raised out of the work. The mill which batters the iron is the Earl of Southampton's. He hath been at a thousand pounds' charge to build it and to fit if for this work.[8]

However, it seems that no more than a token quantity of tinplate was made, the abandonment of the project following soon after the death of the Earl of Southampton in 1624 and the consequential cessation of his patronage.

Whether or not any attempts were made at manufacturing tinplate in Britain during the period between 1624 and 1660 is a matter of supposition but if so all proved unsuccessful. Insufficient technical expertise amongst those seeking to master the process seems to have been the principal reason for the failures as the secrets of the German tinplate makers had yet to be fully acquired and understood by their

English counterparts. Nonetheless, the early 1600's witnessed a revival of interest in the establishment of a tinplate industry in Britain. Amongst other speculators, a group of businessmen which included a few representatives of the Midland iron trade (notably the Baldwins and the Foleys) and a London tinware maker commissioned Andrew Yarranton, a one-time linen draper and enterprising soldier, to visit Saxony for the purpose of acquiring details of the process from the German manufacturers. Aided by an iron works furnaceman as technical adviser and an interpreter Yarranton journeyed to Saxony where, as he subsequently reported: 'Contrary to our expectations we had much liberty to view and see the works go, and the manner of them working and extending the plates, and also the perfect view of such materials as they used in cleaning the plates to make them fit to take tin and with the way they use to tin them over, when cleared from their rust and blackness'.[9]

At the time of Yarranton's visit to Saxony, both the Midland's iron and the Cornish tin trades had entered a period of recession. On returning to England he promoted the idea that the distressed condition of the workers in these industries could be relieved by the establishment of a British tinplate industry. In his report 'England's Improvement by Sea and Land' Yarranton commented:

> God and Nature hath fitted us with two most advantageous minerals in this Nation. One of these rich (yet neglected) minerals is our Tinn in Cornwall . . . I had often designed to get that Trade for making Tinn-plates into England, but never could find out by any the way of making them . . .

> And if convenient Works were set up there for working of Tinn-plates, I know in a short time there might be twenty thousand men employed in that Manufacture . . . and thereby a great Exported Trade will be made into Foreign parts . . .[10]

As shall be seen later, Yarranton's statement presents us with a remarkably perceptive view of the future status of the British tinplate industry.

Obviously, financial support was necessary for the venture to operate during the early stages of development and indeed it would appear that sufficient funds were made available by unknown sources as subsequent reports indicate that a considerable quantity of Forest of Dean iron plates was experimentally coated with Cornish tin and tested by experienced tinsmiths; they found the tinplates produced to be of a quality superior to those of the German manufacturers.

Whilst the technical feasibility of manufacturing tinplate of a standard acceptable to the tinsmiths had been proven by Andrew Yarranton his success did not stimulate, at least to any great extent, others to follow suit. Several petitions for patents to manufacture tinplate were filed and a few granted in the period subsequent to Yarranton's visit but reports in 1697 and again in 1703 indicate that no domestic tinplate was being manufactured and that the British tinsmiths continued to rely on Germany for their supplies. The overriding reason for the lack of entrepreneurial interest appears to have been the cheapness of the tinplate imported from Germany where the combined effects of relatively large scale production and skilled labour minimised production costs. A means of countering the price advantage of German tinplate was necessary if the British industry was to establish a firm hold on the domestic market. This problem of the price uncompetitiveness of British tinplate to a large extent was resolved when the Government, concerned over the future for the British iron industry, in 1703 and 1704 legislated for the introduction of the Subsidy Acts. By means of these, import rates in general were raised including that on imported tinplate. The tariff increase, from eight pence (3p) to five shillings and three pence (26p) per hundred on single sheets and from one shilling and four pence (7p) to ten shillings and six pence (52½p) per hundred on double sheets, offered sufficient protection for a few enterprising manufacturers to re-commence tinplate making in Britain.[11]

Though the precise date of its foundation is unknown, the British tinplate industry certainly flourished in the post Subsidy Acts period. A short-lived tinplate manufacturing enterprise was set up at Bisham-on-Thames, near Great Marlow in Buckinghamshire, production at this works having ceased by 1711.[12] Despite the premature failure of this venture contemporary reports indicate that by the second decade of the eighteenth century the demands of the English tinsmiths were being met more and more by home produced tinplate. An entry in the reports of The Company of Tinplate Workers (viz the tinsmiths) dated 1st November 1726 states: 'Ordered that a representation of the badness of the tinplates marked CGB be drawn up and made to the makers of the said plates'.[13] The obvious conclusion to be drawn from this report is that those engaged in tinplate manufacture in Britain at this point in time still lacked the skills needed to be able supply the market with good quality plates. However, it would appear that these deficiencies were quickly corrected for in 1730 Bishop Watson commented as follows on tinplates used at Lynn in Norfolk: 'The tin men at the first introduction of the English plates were greatly delighted with them; they had a better colour and were more pliable than the foreign ones'. [14]

In the absence of any contradictory evidence it can be assumed that the tinplates referred to in the report of the Company of Tinplate Workers and that of Bishop Watson were made at Pontypool in what is now the County of Gwent. Activity in tinplate making at this time appears to have been confined exclusively to the Pontypool area which, consequently and justifiably, can claim to be the cradle of British tinplate industry. Not only was this an event of significance for Britain but also, and perhaps more importantly, for the Principality for thereby was established the 'Welsh Connection'.

NOTES

[1] Hawthorne, J.G. and Smith C.S., *On Diverse Acts: The Treatise of Theophilus* (University of Chicago Press, 1963).

[2] British Steel plc Archives: *The Steel Company of Wales Ltd.*

[3] Minchinton, W., *The British Tinplate Industry: A History* (Oxford University Press, 1957).

[4] Public Records Office, E190/122/10.

[5] Minchinton, W., op. cit.

[6] Yarranton, A., *England's Improvement by Sea and Land* (London, 1681).

[7] Minchinton, W., op. cit.

[8] Kidderminster Public Library, *Knight Mss.*

[9] Yarranton, A., op. cit.

[10] Ibid.

[11] 6th March 1706/7, *Journal of the House of Commons* (XV325).

[12] Jenkins, Rhys, *The Early Days of the Tinplate Industry* (*Transactions of the Neath Antiquarian Society,* 1930/31).

[13] Document in the Records of the Company Tinplate Workers, 1st November 1726.

[14] Bishop Watson, *Chemical Essays*, Vol. IV (5th Ed. 1796).

2. THE WELSH CONNECTION

Five years have past, five summers, with the length of
five long winters! and again I hear
These waters, rolling from their mountain-springs
With a soft inland murmur.—Once again
Do I behold these steep and lofty cliffs.
That on a mild secluded scene impress
Thoughts of more deep seclusion, and connect
The landscape with the quiet of the sky.

William Wordsworth

(Lines composed a few miles above Tintern Abbey, on revisiting the
banks of the Wye during a Tour, 13th July, 1798.)

For centuries the natural resources of the former County of
Monmouthshire (now Gwent) have been exploited by man for the
manufacture of iron. The landscape, one of high ground covered with
thick forests through which fast flowing rivers and streams cut their
way to the sea, complemented the physical requirements of the early
smelting process. The forested areas yielded up wood for conversion
into the charcoal used to fuel the smelting furnaces. Iron-stone, the
raw material of iron manufacture, was available in reasonably accessible
deposits from the steep sided valleys incised by river erosion. The
rivers themselves provided the power necessary for the operation of
the furnace bellows and for driving the forging hammers.

In all probability it was the Silures, the Celtic tribe of the area, who
first utilised these resources to manufacture iron. The Romans, too,
worked the metal at Monmouth, Hadnock, Trellech, Caerleon and
Lower Machen and built up a fairly intensive industry. Little evidence
exists of iron-making activity during the Dark Ages but in the period
following the Norman Conquest three forges are known to have
operated within the County town itself. Later reports (notably that by
an Exchequer Special Commission published in the final decade of the
sixteenth century) commented on ironworks operations at Machen,
Abercarn, Pontymoel, Monkswood, Tintern, Glyn Ebbw and Pontypool.
It was at the Pontypool Works that subsequent developments were to
have profound consequences for the tinplate industry and its association
with South Wales.

Major John Hanbury.

Appreciating the natural facilities of the area Richard Hanbury—a Worcestershire industrialist with an involvement in the London gold and banking trades—joined Edward Brode, also of Worcestershire, and Edmund Roberts of the Machen Works in a partnership that on 12th July 1526 leased from the Earl of Pembroke certain parcels of land, mainly consisting of woodland, one of which covered of 846 acres adjacent to the then hamlet of Pontypool.[1]

In the following year Hanbury, together with Brode, erected a furnace and forge at Pentrefelyn, Pontypool, and by doing so began the association between the Hanbury family and South East Wales that has continued for over four hundred years.

Richard Hanbury died in 1608. He was succeeded initially in the iron making business by his nephew and later by his nephew's son, Capel Hanbury. Capel Hanbury was not only an astute businessman but also an innovative manufacturer of iron based products. It is generally accepted that it was he who in 1682 introduced to Pontypool the process of rolling bar iron into sheets. This was achieved by repeatedly passing the bar when red hot between a pair of water powered rollers, the gap between the top and bottom rolls being reduced in stages by the rollerman jamming a series of wooden chocks between the roll housings and the necks of the rolls. Capel Hanbury's early experiments with the device were continued by his son, Major John Hanbury, who conceived the idea of using a screw mechanism to reduce the gap between the rolls instead of the unwieldy chock. In the development work both father and son benefited from the experience of very capable works managers viz Thomas Cooke, Edward Allgood and John Payne.[2]

Contemporary reports support the claim that the machinery for rolling bar iron into sheet was perfected by the Hanburys at Pontypool. Notable amongst these reports is that written by Edward Llwyd, the Welsh traveller and reporter. Having visited the Pontypool works and observed the process, in a letter dated 15th June 1697 he commented that: 'One Major Hanbury of this Pont-y-Pool shew'd us an excellent invention of his own, for driving hot iron (by the help of a Rolling Engin mov'd by water) into as thin plates as tin'.[3]

The blackplate (the name given to the untinned sheets) so produced was said by Llwyd to have been made by Hanbury into 'furnaces, pots, kettles, saucepans etc. at a very cheap rate (about the third part of what is usual)'. Despite their early successes it was not until 1728 that John Hanbury and his then Works Manager, John Payne, were granted a patent for the 'art of expanding bars by means of compressing cylinders'.[4] The date when blackplate produced by the rolling method was first used for tinplate manufacture cannot be determined with any certainty for the available evidence is conflicting. Notices declaring the Hanbury's enterprise to be the 'Pontypool Iron and Tinplate Company' were published as early as 1703[5] whilst a further and later statement tells us that: 'About the year 1720 a works for the manufacture of tinplate was established at Pontypool'.[6] Uncertainty there may be over the date of the event but no doubt whatsoever surrounds the fact that Capel Hanbury's achievement in developing a powered rolling mill for the conversion of iron bar into sheet for subsequent tinning was the springboard for the launching of the Welsh tinplate industry.

Despite the appreciable cost and quality benefits associated with the rolling, as opposed to hammering, of iron into sheet the practice was not adopted with alacrity by others engaged in the iron trade. Eventually, however, a few enterprising industrialists realised that

24

'rolled' tinplate was a product with good market potential and they soon converted existing iron forges to the new process. Others constructed entirely new works in which to make the tinplate increasingly in demand by the tinsmiths. These new works were sited as far apart as Rotherham in Yorkshire and Woolard in Somerset but with the main areas of concentration being South Wales and West Gloucestershire as a unit and, to lesser extent, the West Midlands.

In these regions were to be found the earlier-established iron forges that produced bar iron, the base material for tinplate manufacture, and labour skilled in the techniques of iron working. Its proximity to the Cornish tin resources and the availability of port facilities (enabling the import of tin and export of finished tinplate to be undertaken by the quickest and cheapest method of transport for bulk cargoes available in the eighteenth century) made South Wales a particularly advantageous location for the further establishment of tinplate 'manufacturies' and by the mid-eighteenth century tinplate was being produced at the Ponthir (Caerleon) Works and works at Kidwelly, Ynyspenllwch (Swansea Valley), Ynysygerwn (Vale of Neath), Melingriffith (Cardiff), Llechryd (Cardigan), Carmarthen and Caerleon.[7]

Melingriffith Works, Whitchurch, Cardiff (c. 1900).

The output from these works slowly, but nonetheless positively, weakened the hitherto unrelenting hold that overseas manufacturers had over the British market for tinplate. Evidence of the decline in the quantities of tinplate imported from the European mainland is available from eighteenth century port records: in 1710 imports of tinplate into Britain amounted to 2.1 million sheets but by 1760, when a mere 2,700 sheets were imported, physical and technical advancements within the British industry had virtually wiped out what had been a lucrative market for the continental producers.[8] But the growth in output from Britain's tinplate works continued beyond the level at which home demand was satisfied. New outlets for the product needed to be sought out if expansion was to continue apace. By the mid-eighteenth century efforts made to convince overseas consumers of tinplate of the suitability of the British product for their requirements achieved some success and so began the export trade on which the industry's subsequent expansion was founded. Shipping records for the year 1790 confirm the existence of an export trade in British tinplate with, amongst others, Holland, Flanders, France and Italy.[9]

Spain, too, imported tinplate from Britain around this time and it was here that an interesting and unusual use was made of tinplate sheets. One of the most important groups of pictures by the Spanish artist, Goya, was painted on tinplate. Goya executed these works in the period 1793-94. Exactly two centuries later the paintings were subject to a detailed examination before being exhibited in Madrid, London and Chicago. The examination revealed the tinplate coating on the exposed reverse side to be in remarkably good condition, showing only slight traces of corrosion. Many of these paintings are permanently housed in Spain but one, entitled 'Interior of a Prison', is to be seen at the Bowes Museum, Barnard Castle, County Durham.

Goya was appointed Court Painter to George III in 1786 and may have chanced upon tinplate whilst working in that capacity. With little tinplate being manufactured in mainland Europe during the last decade of the eighteenth century and evidence of British (or more precisely, Welsh as over 80% of British tinplate was made in Welsh Works at that time) tinplate exports to Spain in 1790 it can be claimed with a reasonable degree of confidence that the material used by Goya came from this country. The fact that Goya needed a fairly flat surface on which to work lends further support to the claim that he used British made tinplate as the continental manufacturers, and particularly the

Germans, had yet to adopt the rolling mill practice, common in Britain by that time, which produced a much flatter sheet than that achieved under the head of a tilt hammer.

Throughout this early period, tinplate works in the main were no more than appendages to the earlier established iron forges of South Wales. Almost without exception works at which facilities for tinplate manufacture were being introduced already possessed the equipment for forging bar iron. Typically, the Ynyspenllwch Works in the Swansea Valley and the Ynysygerwn Works in the neighbouring Neath Valley, both of which at one stage (from 1780 to about 1799) came into the hands of the Miers family of Neath, were iron forges supplying a local demand for ironware before being adapted for tinplate manufacture. Over the thirty years from 1730 to 1760 the foundations for the establishment of a British industry, laid at Pontypool, were consolidated by a small but steady increase in the number of works producing tinplate and by the beginning of the nineteenth century Britain had a total of sixteen tinplate works, eleven of which were situated in Wales.[10]

By this time, the centre of the domestic market for tinplate had moved from London to the Midlands where new plant had been laid down for the manufacture of domestic articles i.e. pots, pans, kettles and in particular storage containers made out of tinplate. The appeal of tinplate containers for the storage of tea, coffee, confectionery etc. increased sharply during the first half of the eighteenth century, primarily for reasons of their price competitiveness (it was reported in 1763 that good tinware was 'perhaps the cheapest commodity in England in proportion to its use')[11] and decorative features achieved by a technique known as Japanning, imported into Britain from the Orient during the seventeenth century. The designers and decorators of Japan-ware were skilled craftsmen and artists capable of producing articles of such good quality that sometimes the functional purpose became secondary to the aesthetic qualities. Some fine examples of this imitation oriental lacquer-work, in typical black and gold colouring, produced at the Pontypool Japan-ware factory (established by Edward Allgood in 1730) are to be found in the Newport and Pontypool museums.

Coinciding with the expansion of the domestic market was an increased level of demand from overseas, especially from the new territories with America in particular offering the Welsh tinplate manufacturers trading opportunities of immense potential. With this upswing in demand came fresh investment and thirty-two new works (not all of which were to last for more than a few years) came into operation in the first half of the nineteenth century. But even against the background of a continuing upward trend in opportunities for sales these were not always good times for tinplate producers; a period of trade buoyancy in the early 1830's underwent a reversal during the seven years from 1837 to 1844 caused mainly by a financial crisis in the USA. The price of British tinplate fell from 47 shillings (£2.37½p) per box in September 1836 to 25 shillings (£1.25p) per box in 1843 before a market recovery in 1845 brought with it a measure of stability and prices settled at around 35 shillings (£1.75p) per box.[12]

By 1843, a total of twenty-three works were active in South Wales; fifteen of these were situated east of Cardiff, three were in the Neath/Port Talbot area, four in the Swansea Valley (i.e. the area between Morriston and Ystalyfera) and one at Carmarthen. Undoubtedly, however, the period of greatest expansion was that between 1850 and 1890 when investors from the emerging middle classes risked their newly acquired wealth in an industry whose growth potential appeared to be both dynamic and unbridled, stimulated by new applications for the product.[13]

The prolific growth rate during these forty years is clearly illustrated in the following table which also serves to emphasise the regional dominance of South Wales over the rest of Britain.

NUMBER AND PERCENTAGE OF TINPLATE WORKS IN SOUTH WALES COMPARED WITH UK TOTAL
(Source: Brooke, E.H., 'Chronology of the Tinplate Works of Great Britain')

YEAR	NO. OF WORKS IN SOUTH WALES	NO. OF WORKS IN U.K. (INC. W. GLOUCS.)	% IN SOUTH WALES
1850	25	35	71
1891	90	98	92

Not only was South Wales the area of greatest concentration in terms of individual tinplate enterprises but also the works built here, almost without exception, were larger than their English counterparts and so contributed a proportionately greater share to the British industry's overall output potential. By way of illustration, an 1880 survey conducted within the trade confirmed that a total of 260 tinplate mills were operationally available within South Wales compared with only 34 in other regions of the United Kingdom.[14] (N.B. Within the trade the 'tinplate mill' was considered to be the primary production unit within a tinplate works. It referred to the Hot Mill by which the iron, or as later, steel bar was rolled into sheet form for the application of a coating of tin at a later stage in the process).

From 1870 onwards tinplate manufacturing activities in South Wales gravitated to the Swansea sub-region, i.e. the area within a 15 miles radius of Swansea, and was located principally in the towns of Llanelli in the west which had seven works, Gorseinon/Loughor which had four, Pontardulais (seven), Morriston (six), Neath/Briton Ferry (eight) and Port Talbot in the east of the sub-region having a total of six works. In this locality, the availability of coal, navigable rivers (facilitating the easy importation of raw tin and export of finished tinplate), adequate supplies of water for the process and labour that had gained experience of factory conditions through employment in the earlier established, but then declining, copper industry were the

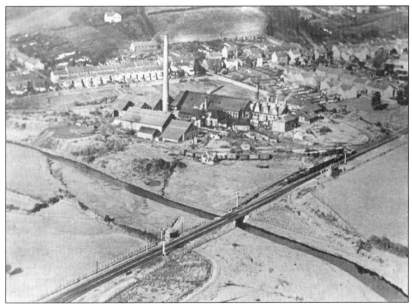

Hendy (near Pontardulais) Tinplate Works, built 1866 (photographed c. 1925).

Worcester Tinplate Works, Morriston, built 1868 (photographed c. 1900).

Aerial view of Port Talbot Docks c. 1940. Baldwin's Steelworks dominates the picture but the Ffrwdwyllt Tinplate Works is to be seen in the right hand corner (steam can be seen rising from the buildings of the works).

elements that proved attractive to tinplate manufacturers. Furthermore, supplies of the sulphuric acid used in the pickling stage of the tinplate manufacturing process were available as a by-product of copper smelting.

But perhaps the one feature that above all others finally gained South Wales universal acknowledgement as the premier tinplate producing region was the 1867 development of open-hearth steelmaking by William Siemens at Landore, Swansea, and the application of steel to tinplate manufacture, perfected by Siemens and his team in collaboration with Daniel Edwards of the Dyffryn Works, Morriston. With its improved properties Open Hearth steel soon gained the favour of the tinplate makers over iron as the base metal. New steel and tinplate works were erected in close proximity to one another and in turn these became the nuclei for the expansion of the towns of Llanelli, Gorseinon, Morriston, Pontardawe, Neath, Briton Ferry and Port Talbot during this period.

However, fundamental to the growth of any industry is the buoyancy of the market for its products and tinplate is no exception to the rule. New markets and applications for tinplate were needed to support further growth; one that emerged in the first half of the nineteenth century—the packaging of food—was to have a profound effect not only on the market for tinplate but also on society at large.

Over the period when tinplate was used mostly for the manufacture of durable household goods, expansion was steady but undramatic. The concept of a Frenchman named Nicholas Appert, when applied to the tinplate trade, altered the entire course of the industry. Appert, a skilled chef, responded to a challenge laid down by the French Government for an alternative to sugar as a means of preserving fruit. In 1809 he suggested that the fresh produce be placed in sealed containers (initially glass) and boiled whilst in the container, the seal of which should remain intact until the contents were required for consumption.[15]

This suggestion eventually came to the attention of an English marchant by the name of Durand who must have been impressed with the potential of the technique for in 1810 he secured a patent on Appert's process. In the statement supporting the patent application Durand reported: 'First, I place and enclose the said food or articles in bottles or other vessels of glass, pottery, tin or other metal or fit materials'.[16] Here, in this statement, was the first indication that

31

Aerial view of Gorseinon c. 1930. Just above the centre line is the Gorseinon Tinplate Works with the Grovesend Tinplate Works slightly above and to the right. In the top left-hand corner is the Grovesend Steel Works and in the bottom right corner is the Bryngwyn Steel Works and Sheet Mills.

tinplate containers could be used for the preservation of food. In 1811, Durand sold his patent rights to the firm of Donkin, Hall and Gamble for the sum of £1,000. Further experiments were conducted by the firm into various methods of preserving food in sealed containers. During these trials glass jars with cork seals were found to be ineffective as preserving vessels because of the fragility of the glass and the porosity of the cork and so attention turned to canisters made out of tinplate as an alternative medium for food preservation vessels.

Undoubtedly, the new 'canisters'—sheared out of tinplate, shaped and soldered along the seams—were a success as subsequently Donkin, Hall and Gamble founded a factory in Bermondsey, London as a large scale 'Preservatory' in which the canisters were manufactured, filled with their contents, sealed and then sterilised by immersion in boiling water.

Convinced that the new product would find a ready market in the armed forces in an enterprising move Donkin, Hall and Gamble sent samples of their wares to noted public figures, many of whom had strong military connections. One sample was sent to Lord Wellesley (later the Duke of Wellington) who through his secretary in response commented: 'I am therefore desired by his Lordship to inform you, that the preserved beef which you were pleased to send him for trial, he found very good, and that as far as he can form an opinion from this trial, he is induced to think that your new method of preserving provisions may be usefully employed for the services of the Navy and Army'.[17]

The Royal Navy quickly realised the potential of canned foods as a means of providing a welcome alternative to the seafarers' traditional diet of hard tack and salted meat and became the Preservatory's initial customer of any significance. Soon, tinplate canisters containing food were proving their worth in exceptional climatic conditions when they were used by Sir Edward Parry's 1824 expedition in search of the North West passage. Expedition reports confirm the effectiveness of canned foods as a convenient source of sustenance for Parry and his colleagues whilst challenging the rigours of the Polar conditions. Nine years later, Captain John Ross led a similar expedition to the area and recovered a number of items left by Parry at Fury Sound. Amongst them was a can of meat which Ross and his descendants retained in their possession until 1958 when it was opened under strictly monitored conditions. When examined by experts the contents were

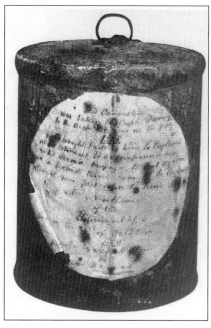
Can of roast veal, 1824.

found to be in a remarkably well preserved state, even after 134 years
—an impressive testimony to the effectiveness of tinplate canisters for
food preservation.[18]

Soon, Britain's Merchant Navy followed its Royal counterpart and
began to use canned foods to help sustain ship's crews and passengers
over long sea journeys. But surprisingly it was not until the year 1830
that food packed in sterile tinplate containers reached retail outlets.
Price appears to have been the primary prohibitive factor, each can
having to be hand made by experienced tinsmiths in a skilful but slow
operation. The unmechanised and labour intensive nature of U.K. can-
making practices in the first half of the nineteenth century meant that
the cost benefits normally associated with mass production remained
unrealised. Also, in a small maritime country with an advancing
agricultural industry such as Britain where fresh meat, fish and
vegetables were fairly readily and regularly available, the attractions
of canned foods were insufficient to create a high demand despite
offering out-of-season or new varieties of produce.

However, the market conditions prevailing in the United States of

America in the second half of the nineteenth century were vastly different from those existing in Britain. The economic potential of the enormous land mass of the American continent was subjected to positive exploitation through immigrant settlement on a massive scale. The intrepid early pioneers and those who in their droves followed in their trail required sustenance during their long-distance treks. Having arrived at their destination, the immediate concern of the settlers in the new centres of population in the mid and western States was the provision of food. Obviously, nature was the initial provider but climatic conditions, both seasonal and geographical, limited the availability of fresh foods. A supplementary and convenient means of food provisioning in mass quantities was therefore neccesary to support the on-going settlement process taking place within the North American Continent. Food packed in tinplate canisters offered the ideal solution for in this form it was easily transportable and remained safe and edible even after long periods of storage. American manufacturers, financially supported by entrepreneurs who realised the business potential of this vast and insatiable market, soon developed the machinery by which cans could be manufactured, filled and sealed on an unprecedented scale.

Can of carrots and gravy taken on
Sir Edward Parry's Arctic
exploration in 1824.

Can from Sir Edward Belcher's
Arctic Expedition in 1852.

During its period of infancy the American canning industry depended entirely on supplies of tinplate manufactured in Europe. To meet the consequential growth in demand, tinplate production in Britain increased from 4,000 tons in 1805 to 37,000 tons in 1850. Twenty years later output had risen to 150,000 tons—a fourfold increase on the 1850 level, a rate of expansion maintained over the two decades preceding 1890 when production amounted to a staggering 586,000 tons.

Exports, likewise, rose dramatically from a mere 25,000 tons in 1850 to 118,000 tons in 1872 peaking at 448,379 tons in 1891 when a high proportion, i.e. 72% or 325,000 tons, of total United Kingdom production was delivered into the American market. As these figures testify, can makers and other users of tinplate in the USA relied heavily on Britain for their supplies; equally the British tinplate industry needed a vigorous outlet for its increasing production capability and that it found in the USA.

Throughout the penultimate decade of the nineteenth century the volume of trade with overseas countries maintained the buoyancy of the Welsh industry. The upwards trend in demand continued until 1891 when output peaked at 690,000 tons with exports at 448,000 tons accounting for 65% of the total U.K. tinplate production.[19]

Can of tripe, c. 1880.

Inevitably, the combined effects of an expanding market and the profitability of many tinplate companies encouraged further capital investment; existing works were enlarged and a number of new works built in South Wales between 1880 and 1890. Sixteen of these new works were erected in South West Wales, accelerating the earlier established westwards migration of the industry from its hitherto traditional base in South East Wales. The extent of the westward migration of the industry, with the Swansea sub-region becoming the new focal point, is shown in the following table:

NUMBER OF TINPLATE WORKS AND MILLS 1875-1905

LOCATION	NO. OF WORKS				NO. OF MILLS	
	1875	1885	1891	1905	1891	1905
Mid, South and West Glamorgan	27	44	54	46	277	266
Gwent	16	20	15	11	86	50
Dyfed	14	17	21	18	119	105
Rest of Britain	20	17	8	8	43	32
TOTAL	77	98	98	83	525	453

As previously stated, the over-riding factor influencing the consolidation of South West Wales as the new centre of tinplate manufacture within the Principality was the successful application of steel to tinplate manufacture. The earliest reported use of steel for making tinplate was that by Messrs Phillips and Smith at their works in Dafen, Llanelli in 1856, the steel used having been produced at the Dowlais Iron and Steel Works by the Converter method developed by Henry Bessemer.[20] Although some good quality plates were made the venture proved to be commercially unsuccessful. The precise reasons for the failure are not known but it may be assumed (from experience gained later by tinplate manufacturers in using Bessemer steel) that inconsistencies in the quality of the steel made by Henry Bessemer's Convertor method resulted in the generation of unacceptably high quantities of sub-standard material. If only the quality problems could be eliminated steel, with properties superior to those found in iron, would provide tinplate manufacturers with an ideal base material.

Sir William Siemens.

Sir William Siemens, initially having worked on developing the regenerative open-hearth furnace in Birmingham, successfully applied the principle to steelmaking at Landore, Swansea in 1869. A much slower process than the rival Converter method of Henry Bessemer, the longer processing time enabled the furnaceman to exercise greater control over operating parameters to ensure a better quality product. Siemens steel made at the Landore Works was first tried for tinplate manufacture in 1876, the trials being held at the Llangennech Works, Llanelli and, significantly, at the Dyffryn Works, Morriston. The suggestion of using Open-Hearth steel for tinplate making was raised in 1874 by Phelps, James & Co., Liverpool based international agents in the metal trades and owners of the Llangennech Works, Llanelli. The New York office of Phelps, James & Co. subsequently placed orders for tinplate made from Open-Hearth Steel both on the Llangennech Works and on the Dyffryn Works.. Daniel Edwards, the founder-owner of the Dyffryn Works, co-operated with Siemens and his team at Landore (principally James Riley, Works Manager and Arthur Willis, Chief Chemist) in the development work. It would seem that Siemens's choice of Edwards as his collaborator was not merely

38

because of the close proximity of the Dyffryn Works to Landore but also for reasons of the latter's knowledge and expertise in tinplate manufacture, for later he said of Edwards: 'With the assistance of Mr. Daniel Edwards, I have overcome many difficulties and have succeeded in making steel tinplate bars'.[21]

The significance of this development was that tinplate manufacturers, previously dependent for the success of their businesses on supplies of iron bar of somewhat variable quality, soon had available to them a base material of greater strength than iron and, perhaps more importantly, of a consistently higher standard of quality. This resulted in lower tinplate reduction costs; in 1880 William Flower of the Melyn Works in Neath claimed a reduction in manufacturing costs of 4% could be gained if steel plate was used in place of iron. The success of the Siemens/Edwards experiments stimulated the construction of a number of steelworks with open-hearth furnaces in the Llanelli/ Swansea/Port Talbot region between 1876 and 1900 when fourteen were in existence, principally in support of tinplate production. Steel manufactured by the Open-Hearth process, whilst taking longer (6 to 8

Daniel Edwards of the Dyffryn Works, Morriston.

hours per charge), and more costly to produce than Bessemer steel (15 to 20 minutes per charge) continued to receive the favour of the majority of tinplate producers even though most of the quality problems associated with the Bessemer process were eventually overcome through further development work.[22]

The adoption of the Bessemer method of steelmaking by a few of the early ironworks built on the northern edge of the South Wales Coalfield (notably Dowlais in Glamorgan and Ebbw Vale in Monmouthshire), committed tinplate manufacturers in East Wales, previously reliant on the local ironworks for their supplies of bar iron, to using Bessemer steel bar unless prepared to meet the extra costs of transporting Siemens steel bars from South West Wales.

In a number of cases, that was a cost they were prepared to incur in order to obtain the better quality product and so, in overall terms, the industry depended more on supplies of Siemens steel than of Bessemer steel until well into twentieth century.

The Welsh tinplate manufacturers expansionist policies, dynamically implemented throughout the eighteenth and nineteenth centuries, underwent a dramatic and unparalleled reversal before the turn of the century. Already entering a period of recession because of domestic economic conditions, the industry was dealt a severe financial and political blow in 1890 when the American Congress, exhorted by Congressman McKinley (later Governor of Ohio), passed the McKinley Act which imposed a tariff on inter alia all tinplate imported into the USA. In effect, the tariff of 2.2 cents per pound weight raised the cost of tinplate manufactured in Wales and destined for the American market by ten shillings and two pence per box (51p)—a 70% increase on the then selling price of fourteen shillings and four pence (71½p) per box.[23] (It should be noted that, traditionally, tinplate has been sold by area [not weight] in 'boxes'. Initially, the standard box of tinplate comprised 112 sheets of size 20 inches by 14 inches = 31,360 square inches. Twenty boxes of tinplate weighed approximately one ton.)

The purpose of the tariff was simple: it was introduced to protect the emerging American tinplate industry and little doubt surrounds its success in meeting the objective of its sponsors for it matched the effectiveness of the British Subsidy Acts of 1703 and 1704 in building a protective barrier behind which an infant tinplate industry could develop.

40

William McKinley campaigning in 1890, whilst Congressman for Ohio, for the introduction of a tariff on all tinplate imported into the U.S.A.

Following its imposition in July 1891, the tariff forced the Welsh tinplate manufacturers to reduce prices in the hope of retaining a sizeable portion of the American business. The selling price offered by the Welsh tinplaters fell alarmingly and stood at no more than ten shillings and five pence farthing (52½p) a box by 1893—a fall of 27% on the pre-tariff prices.[24] Inevitably, the fall in prices and tougher market conditions forced into liquidation companies whose manufacturing practices were inefficient or whose financial standing lacked soundness. Every effort was made to keep a company solvent and indeed during periods of financial difficulties for their employers, workers sometimes remained loyal and continued to work and maintain production even though they knew they would receive little or no payment for their labours. Richard Thomas, the founder of the company that bore his name, was assisted in this manner when his firm was in its infancy as were the owners of the Baglan Bay, Landore and the Raven (Glanamman) Works.[25] Nonetheless, thirty-six Welsh

41

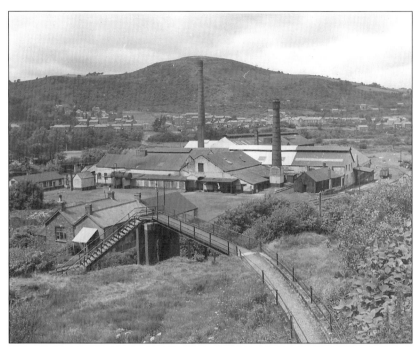

Glanrhyd Tinplate Works, Pontardawe. Built in 1879 and acquired by William
Gilbertson & Co. in 1883 for £7,500.

tinplate companies had no alternative but to cease operations during
the period 1896 to 1899. Despite this setback, only six works were to
remain permanently closed, the rest having been taken over and
reopened by new companies when trade improved—a common feature
of the industry in the early days when the assets of a company in
liquidation could be acquired by a rival firm for a relatively low capital
outlay. For example, in 1883 the Glanrhyd (Pontardawe) works,
consisting of three mills and associated equipment, was acquired by
the Gilbertsons—a family concern with substantial steel and tinplate
manufacturing interests in the Swansea Valley—from the previous
owners, the Glantawe Tin Plate Co. for the sum of £7,500. Immediately, the Gilbertson's registered a new company, the Glanrhyd Tin
Plate Co., with capital of £21,000.[26]

Capital funding for tinplate ventures in South Wales came from a
variety of sources—industrialists, steel and tinplate merchants and,

increasingly from the mid-nineteenth century onwards, by means of investment from within the middle classes, reflecting the newly acquired wealth of this emerging social group. Vaughan, a solicitor, at one time leased the Kidwelly Tinplate Works; Downman, an accountant, held shares in the Carmarthen Works whilst a dentist by the name of Winkworth became a partner in the company that operated the Dafen works in Llanelli. The involvement of the South Wales middle class in the tinplate trade is further illustrated by reference to the company operating the Clayton Works at Pontardulais which in 1883 had nineteen shareholders, including seven grocers, two builders, someone described as a 'gentleman' and an hotel proprietor. Llanelli's Burry Tinplate Works had seven shopkeepers, three teachers, two ministers of religion, an accountant, a land agent, a timber merchant and a brick manufacturer amongst the twenty-seven shareholders in its holding company.[27]

The structure of ownership of tinplate companies in South Wales at this time was largely parochial in the sense that the majority of investors lived within the local community. The incentive of a steady, if undramatic, return on capital together with the opportunity for tradespeople to secure an increase in their principal trade either directly (by supplying goods and/or services to the works itself) or indirectly (by putting pressure on workers to use their stores or services) proved to be sufficiently lucrative to attract local investment.

Despite the punitive effect of the McKinley Tariff, the creation of new markets and the rapid expansion of the food canning industry during the early part of the twentieth century reversed the downward trend in the demand for tinplate. In 1905, 396 mills were in operation but enhanced market opportunities meant that the number rose to 472 by 1912 when output reached 848,000 tons and to 550 by 1914. A few months before the commencement of hostilities in the 1914-1918 War the level of demand matched the industry's capacity (i.e. the output from 550 mills). Twelve months earlier the *Economist* had reported that: 'In the Swansea District more capital has been expended in the last seven years than in any corresponding period in the history of the trade'.

NOTES

[1] Clark, A., *The Story of Monmouthshire, Vol. II* (Monnow Press, 1979).

[2] Jenkins, Rhys, op. cit.

[3] Llwyd, Edward, Letter to Dr. Tancred Robinson F.R.S., 15th June 1697 (*Philosophical Transactions,* Vol. XXVII, 1712).

[4] Jenkins, Rhys, op. cit.

[5] Hanbury, John, *Observations on the Making of Iron* (see Gibbs F.W., *Annals of Science*, Vol. VII (1951)).

[6] Dr. Ure in his 'Dictionary', quoted in Clark A., op. cit.

[7] Brooke, E.H., *Chronology of the Tinplate Works of Great Britain* (Cardiff, 1944).

[8] P.R.O., Customs, 3/4-60.

[9] P.R.O., Customs, 3/4-60.

[10] Brooke, E.H., op. cit.

[11] Mortimer, T., *The Universal Directory Part II* (1763).

[12] Minchinton, W., op. cit.

[13] Ibid.

[14] Ibid.

[15] Hedges, E.S., op. cit.

[16] Reader, W.J., *Metal Box: A History* (Heinneman, London, 1976).

[17] Ibid.

[18] Ibid.

[19] Brooke, E.H., op. cit.

[20] Ibid.

[21] Carr, J.C. and Taplin, W., *History of the British Steel Industry* (Basil Blackwell, Oxford, 1962).

[22] Ibid.

[23] Rutherford, R., *Romancing in Tinplate* (Cleveland, Ohio, 1950).

[24] Minchinton, W., op. cit.

[25] Ibid.

[26] Davies, J.H., *History of Pontardawe and District from Earliest to Modern Times* (Christopher Davies, Llandybïe, 1967).

[27] Minchinton, W., op. cit.

3. RE-ORGANISATION AND RE-CONSTRUCTION

In 1924 the American Rolling Mill Company built a mill invented by John B. Tytus, culminating ten years of experimentation. This mill located at the Company's Ashland Plant, was based on sheet practice and its development required accurate determination of many phases of the rolling process as well as the discard of many previously accepted theories and ideas.[1]

Before the Great War, the parochiality and conservatism of the Welsh tinplate manufacturers was clearly evident in their attitude towards change. They believed the method of making tinplate developed and employed in Wales to be unrivalled. Although their attitude to change was more evolutionary than revolutionary even refinements to the customary method of making tinplate suggested by the more progressive amongst them were sometimes treated with scepticism.[2] Throughout the last two decades of the nineteenth century and the first two of the twentieth little regard had been paid to co-operation in either the search for major improvements in manufacturing techniques or the enhancement of marketing ability. Similarly, the introduction of financial arrangements that would ensure a measure of stability during periods of recession and provide for depreciation of plant and equipment were largely ignored.

In many cases control of businesses remained within the families whose forebears had been the founders. In consequence, professional managers, engineers and metallurgists were rarely recruited but even when employed were given little latitude to introduce changes that might have had an influence on the future course of the business. Lacking in confidence and frequently suspicious of his fellow manufacturers, the Welsh tinplate maker's reactionary attitudes hindered any attempt by the more enlightened amongst them to organise a re-structuring of the industry through amalgamations. Described as 'unadventurous, highly individualistic, not markedly adaptable and easily satisfied',[3] the Welsh manufacturers' lack of foresight and enterprise figured prominently in the failure of the domestic industry to meet the challenges presented by the emerging industries of America, France and Germany—a failing that subsequently cost Wales its premier position in the league table of tinplate producing countries.

45

Eventually, the onset of adverse economic conditions concentrated the minds of the tinplate makers on developing a financial and technical reconstruction of the industry that, when implemented, proved to be of an unprecedented magnitude. The first problem tackled was the industry's out-dated commercial practices but only after lengthy and detailed discussions between representatives of the various trade associations was an agreement eventually struck on the imposition of controls over the prices charged for both steel bar and finished tinplate.

With the Welsh industry still heavily reliant on overseas trade, it was soon realised that an orderly system of sales quotas was essential if a 'free-for-all' in world trade in the commodity, with damaging consequences for all concerned, was to be averted. Hence the agreement reached in 1934 with the American, German and French manufacturers—all of whom by this time were rapidly increasing their production potential—known as the 'Tinplate Cartel'. The Cartel provided for the introduction of a quota system which was intended to control the level of exporting to be undertaken by the parties to the agreement. Although the Welsh manufacturers' share of the world export market had fallen to just over double that of their chief rivals, viz. the Americans, the agreement offered, for a while at least, a measure of protection against further decline by fixing at their pre-agreement levels the quantities of tinplate that Britain and the other parties to it individually could export.[4]

The major advancement of the nineteen-twenties was the series of amalgamations, involving several of the major tinplate enterprises, by which the number of small, independent companies was reduced and ownership mainly concentrated within three large groups. Beginning with the Briton Ferry Steel Company's acquisition of the nearby Albion Steelworks in 1914 and their purchase of the Resolven Tinplate Works in 1919, the Ferry Works (Briton Ferry) in 1921, the Aberavon Works (1922) and the Melyn Works at Neath in 1924 (giving the parent company control over 15 tinplate mills) the trend continued with Baldwins Ltd. gaining control of the Port Talbot Steel Company in 1915. In the same year Baldwins constructed the Margam Tinplate Works and later (1920-22) acquired a further fifteen tinplate mills within the Eagle Works (Neath), the Fairwood Works (Gowerton) and the Wern Works at Briton Ferry. A subsequent acquisition of Baldwins Ltd. was the Landore Steelworks at Swansea

Elba Tinplate Works, Swansea. Built in 1925, the last 'old type' tinplate works to be built in Britain.

whilst an entirely new venture was the erection in 1925 of the large Elba Works, containing sixteen tinplate mills, at Crumlin Burrows, Swansea. Owned and operated jointly by Baldwins and the Anglo-Asiatic Petroleum Company, tinplate produced at the Elba Works was destined primarily for the rapidly expanding oil can industry.[5]

Each acquisition or amalgamation represented a step in the direction of a re-organised industry with control vested in large corporations. Of particular significance in this context was the merger between Richard Thomas and Company and the Grovesend Steel and Tinplate Company for it brought to the former the aggressive leadership of William Firth (of whom more shall be said later). The Grovesend Steel and Tinplate Company had itself grown through the acquisition of the Hendy Works (1909) the Amman Works (Garnant) in 1914, the Raven Works (Glanamman) in 1913 and the Whitford Works at Briton Ferry in 1916 (the latter two were steel sheet, not tinplate, works) and shortly after the end of the First World War the company purchased the assets of the Lewis family of Gorseinon for the sum of £25,000. Included in this purchase were two tinplate works (the Cambria, Pontardulais, and the Gorseinon Works) with a total of 12 mills and the Bryngwyn Steel and Sheet Works with 12 sheet mills. By virtue of the 1923 merger with the Grovesend Steel and Tinplate Company and through other acquisitions, Richard Thomas and Company—already a major force within the industry—gained control of 165 tinplate mills, 24 sheet mills and 6 steel works. Interests held in brick, engineering, colliery and marketing concerns indicate that Richard Thomas & Company's expansionism operated on both horizontal and vertical planes.[6]

In a similar manner, soon after the conclusion of the Great War a number of steel, tinplate and colliery concerns based in South East Wales joined together under the title of Partridge, Jones and John Paton Limited. By the end of 1921, this firm had acquired ownership of twenty-two tinplate mills (works at Caerleon, Machen, Pontypool and Pontymister), a steelworks (the Pontymister Works) with seven Open-Hearth furnaces, sixteen sheet mills, a foundry and engineering works together with extensive colliery holdings.

John Paton, originally a merchant selling steel based products, was the prime mover behind the amalgamation process and it was he who became the first chairman of Partridge Jones & John Paton Ltd. whose offices were at 88, Dock Street, Newport.[7]

However, some firms continued in their original form, undisturbed by the movement towards concentrated ownership. In the main these were the smaller family concerns often operating no more than six mills apiece although a few of the medium sized firms, such as Gilbertsons, based at Pontardawe, and the Upper Forest and Worcester Steel and Tinplate Co. Ltd. of Morriston also maintained their independence during this period.

Despite the effects of the General Strike, the British tinplate industry continued to hold onto its premier position amongst tinplate producing countries, resisting the ever-strengthening challenges of America, France and Germany. In 1928, exports from Britain amounted to 64% of the world trade in tinplate. By comparison, exports from the USA stood at 28% of world trade, those from Germany at 5% and France 3%. But the signs were ominous. Advancements in manufacturing techniques and marketing practices introduced by other tinplate producing nations were soon to undermine the dominant position of the Welsh industry. By the late nineteen-thirties Britain's share of the world trade in tinplate had fallen to 42%, the principal challenge coming from America whose new technology had boosted its share to 39%. Germany, too, had become a strong contender capturing 13% of the market with France and Italy each having a 3% share.[8]

It was upon the ingenuity of their engineers and the confidence of their industrialists in the ability of the latter to develop revolutionary methods of rolling and tinning that the American challenge was based. Apart from periodic minor modifications, the method of tinplate manufacture favoured by the Welsh had remained largely unaltered since Hanbury first squeezed heated bar iron through a pair of powered rolls. The inherent productivity shortcomings of the hand mill process—batch and not continuous operations, limited plate sizes, inconsistency in weight, gauge and shape—were not challenged with any great vigour by the Welsh tinplate makers. As one observer commented: 'A Welsh tinplate mill . . . seems as unalterable as the laws of the Medes and Persians. Hanbury or from whomsoever's brain it evolved, like Archimedes, seems to have hit upon the one and only way, for all time, of doing the work contemplated by a sort of inspiration, for no decisive improvements have been brought about since'.[9]

The American tinplate producer shared none of his Welsh counterpart's scepticism over the innovative role of engineers and metallurgists; in Wales the emphasis lay heavily on the experienced layman in contrast to what was happening across the Atlantic where tinplate makers sought to develop and apply in a pioneering manner new concepts which in terms of tinplate manufacture represented a quantum leap forward.

In the States, tinplate users were also seeking new applications for the product. In 1935 tinplate cans made by the American Can Company were filled for the first time with beer, brewed by the G. Kreuger Brewery Company, Newark, New Jersey. A year later, the Felinfoel Brewery Ltd., Llanelli followed the American example. By 1936, the U.K. annual production of beer cans was running at about 2 million, but the wax lining of the cans, which tainted the flavour of their contents, and their cost disadvantage compared with glass bottles resulted in little growth in their use in the U.K. until the outbreak of World War II.[10]

However, in keeping with the dynamic industrial society that existed within the United States in the nineteen twenties and thirties, American engineers set about tackling the problems associated with the production of steel strip on a continuous basis. The first continuous hot strip mill in the world, when successfully brought into operation at Ashland, Kentucky in 1924, was the manifestation of their ingenuity and diligence,. Within five years of the commissioning of the Ashland Mill six smaller hot strip mills were in production in the USA, their operators reaping the benefits of higher outputs, lower costs and improved product quality giving them a clear advantage over their competitors. By 1929 American engineers had also developed and brought into production the world's first continuous cold reduction mill, the function of which was to further reduce the thickness of the hot rolled steel strip by cold rolling (i.,e. the strip remaining unheated whilst being processed) to a gauge suitable for tinplate manufacture.[11]

As a result of these developments the American industry moved rapidly from being labour to being capital intensive; the same could not be said of its Welsh counterpart. The following table depicts the situation in Wales in 1931 and clearly illustrates the dependency on out-dated methods and machinery.

NUMBER OF MILLS, CAPACITIES AND MANNING LEVELS BY COMPANY—1931

(Source: Brooke, E.G., *Chronology of the Tinplate Works of Great Britain*)

COMPANY/GROUP	NO. OF HAND MILLS	CAPACITY PER WEEK	
		(BASIS BOXES)	(TONS)
Richard Thomas & Co. Subsidiaries	212	224,000	10,800
Briton Ferry Steel Co.	48	49,500	2,385
Baldwins Ltd.	43	36,000	1,736
Llanelly Associated Tinplate Co's.	45	48,400	2,314
Partridge, Jones & John Paton Ltd.	21	22,000	1,060
Bynea Steelworks Ltd. Subsidiaries	118	15,000	725
Upper Forest & Worcester Co. Ltd.	16	16,800	810
Remainder	107	120,800	5,824
	499	532,100	25,655

In the same year, nine continuous wide hot strip mills were in operation in the USA, having a gross nominal capacity of 113,000 tons per week. However, only two, viz Weirton Steel (West Virginia) and the Carnegie Illinois Steel Corp. of Gary, Indiana, directly supported tinplate manufacture, the other seven were engaged principally in the rolling of wide strip for the sheet trade.[12]

The Americans assessed the average output of a continuous strip mill to be of the order of 320 tons per shift of eight hours, if manned by 30 men.[13] In comparison, a Staffordshire sheet mill manned by eight men per shift was capable of rolling 4.5 tons in eight hours (sheets of dimensions 76" x 36"); A Welsh sheet mill with seven men per shift could produce 3 tons in eight hours and Welsh tinplate mill producing 20" x 14" (108 lbs substance) size sheets could roll 2.75 tons in eight hours with four men per shift.[14]

However, notwithstanding their apparent parochiality, tinplate makers in Wales were not completely oblivious to the transformation taking place in America. Disturbed by news of the successes of the Americans, the normally complacent Welsh manufacturers sponsored two representatives, Messrs. G.E. Tregonning and H.W. Morgan, to cross the Atlantic in 1928 to see continuous strip rolling at first hand. Reports circulated on their return provided the stimulus for the trade to establish a committee, under the chairmanship of F.W. Gilbertson, charged with the responsibility of examining the feasibility of erecting a Continuous Strip Mill in South Wales. The untimely death of Gilbertson in 1929 combined with the problems of funding such a venture at a time of economic recession brought this initiative to a premature end.[15]

By the mid-thirties the industry's recovery from the ravages of recession was sufficient for interest to be renewed in laying down a strip mill plant in Wales. The principal protagonist was Sir William Firth, Chairman of Richard Thomas & Co., who had reached that position having previously held a similar post with the Grovesend Steel and Tinplate Company. He had joined the latter after having founded and operated a successful London-based merchant firm. It was Firth who, with foresight and determination, not only campaigned vigorously to secure an agreement with his fellow manufacturers providing for the construction and operation of a continuous hot strip mill in South Wales but also tenaciously resisted suggestions by other companies, viz. the Austin Company, United Steel, Dorman Long and

Sir William Firth.

the South Durham Company, that Britain's first strip mill ought not to be erected in the traditional tinplate producing area of South Wales but instead at a location nearer to the Midlands motor vehicles plants that consumed sheet steel in large quantities. Also featuring in the future plans of the South Durham Company was the construction of new plant for tinplate manufacture—a proposition which if carried into effect would have dealt a mortal wound to the Welsh tinplate industry. Fortunately for all those concerned with the trade in the Principality, Firth's lobbying of both the British Iron and Steel Federation and the Government ensured that the South Durham Company did not gain national support and consequently it soon abandoned any plans it had for manufacturing tinplate.[16]

Firth's strongly held views on the need for a re-structuring of the South Wales tinplate industry certainly engendered an attitude of opposition amongst the traditionalists, still content to retain personal control over small, relatively inefficient works. His initiative for a concerted approach to the question of modernisation was coolly received and subsequently repudiated, possibly more for reasons of the traditionalists dislike of what appeared to them to be his egotistical manner than sound economic and technical logic.

Undeterred by this set-back, Firth continued to pursue the realisation of his dream of a Welsh industry able to compete on equal terms with its rivals and eventually he managed to persuade the Board of Richard Thomas and Company to proceed unilaterally with the strip mill project. By 1935, the Company's financial status was considered sound enough to support the unprecedented level of capital expenditure required for such a venture. In July of that year the decision to undertake the construction of the United Kingdom's first strip mill, together with associated equipment, was made public.

Whilst the announcement signalled the commencement of a new chapter in the history of British tinplate manufacture it evoked angry and acrimonious outbursts of rhetoric from within the South Wales tinplate communities. Why should this momentous announcement have been received with such hostility? The answer to this question was that the Company decided to construct the new strip mill and associated tinplate plant (capable of producing 700,000 tons per annum of tinplate and an equal amount of sheet) not in South Wales but in Lincolnshire. The Company's Redbourne Works, where blast furnaces and steel plant were already in operation utilising the resources of the nearby Northamptonshire ore field, was to be the recipient of the new mill.[17]

Although the choice of the Redbourne site may have seemed justifiable to Richard Thomas & Co. on grounds of product cost, the social and economic consequences of the decision for South Wales were immense, almost beyond comprehension. Besides the thirty thousand directly employed in the industry many more were engaged in ancillary activities e.g. steelworks, miners, chemical workers, not forgetting transport and docks personnel. Many voices, representative of both sides of the industrial community and shades of political opinion within the region, soon were united in opposition. The Mayor of Swansea, Alderman W.J. Davies, led a delegation of tradespeople and union representatives to a meeting with the President of the Board of Trade, Walter Runciman, in the hope of impressing upon him the seriousness with which the Redbourne decision was viewed in South Wales.[18] Almost immediately the Prime Minister, Stanley Baldwin, intervened —undoubtedly an action that had a considerable influence in bringing about a change of heart amongst the Directors of Richard Thomas &

Company. For within four months of the July 1935 statement the Company announced that the new strip mill was not to be built as originally intended at Redbourne but in South Wales. The chosen location was Ebbw Vale and the strip mill was to be built in tandem with a complete re-construction of the existing, but by then out-dated and idle, iron and steel works in the town.

The extent to which the Board members of Richard Thomas & Co. were influenced in their initial choice of Redbourne by their disillusionment over the intransigence of the other South Wales tinplate makers cannot be established, but it is reasonable to assume that amongst such a group of experienced businessman emotions would have been suppressed in favour of sound business sense. Whatever the reason, a sense of relief prevailed within the South Wales tinplate communities when the decision was reversed in favour of Ebbw Vale. The choice of Ebbw Vale ahead of a site in South West Wales was principally for reasons of the availability locally of raw materials i.e. coking coal, limestone and water (only iron ore had to be brought to the area) and the existing, but by then de-commissioned, blast furnaces (2) and steelmaking plant at the Works owned by Richard Thomas & Co. But the over-riding factor was the offer of state financial assistance for the project, forthcoming as a consequence of the district being regarded in Government circles as economically depressed and an unemployment 'black spot'. Ironically, it was later realised that most of the unemployed in the area were coal miners and that many of those who eventually gained employment at the Works were migrants from the steel and tinplate works of South West Wales. Construction work began in 1936 and the new hot strip mill was brought into operation in September 1938. The tinning process employed at the Works remained unaltered from the 'old style' tin pots, although by then they were highly mechanised.

Just before and during the Second World War production ceased at a number of the old, inefficient works. Many of those forced into idleness were subsequently requisitioned by the Ministry of Supply for the storage of the materials of war and works falling into this category were the Aberdulais (Neath), Beaufort (Morriston), Bryn (Pontardawe), Caerleon, Cambria (Pontardulais), Copper Miners (Cwmafan), Morfa (Llanelli) and Ynyscedwyn at Ystalyfera. However, this phase of closures was merely a prelude to the major re-organisation of the late nineteen-forties and early fifties that was to completely transform the structure of the Welsh tinplate industry.[19]

The Hot Strip Mill installed at Ebbw Vale Works and Sir William Firth (inset).

The next step towards a re-structured industry capable of meeting customers' demands for a better quality, low cost product was taken in 1945 when the two giants of the trade, viz. Richard Thomas and Company and Baldwins Limited, amalgamated—an event that brought 340 out of the then 500 hand mills in the trade under single control.

The new company, Richard Thomas and Baldwins Limited, was interested in erecting a second strip mill in South Wales but hesitant about funding the venture in isolation. Several other firms with interests in iron, steel and tinplate manufacture were approached with the view to participating in the scheme and after lengthy discussions and deliberations three companies viz. Guest Keen Baldwins Limited, (who owned and operated a steel plant at Port Talbot), John Lysaght (a producer of steel sheet at the Orb Works, Newport) and the Llanelly Associated Tinplate Companies (owners and operators of steel and tinplate works in the Llanelli area) joined with Richard Thomas and Baldwins to form The Steel Company of Wales Limited, incorporated on the 2nd May 1947 under the chairmanship of Mr. (later Sir) Ernest Lever. Capital funding from both private and public (i.e. the

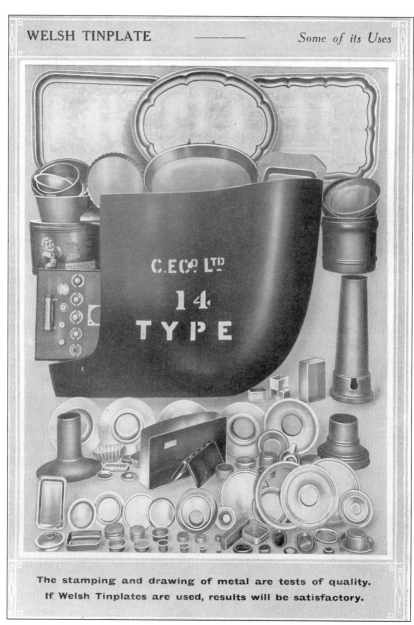

C.E.C⁰. L™
14·
TYPE

The stamping and drawing of metal are tests of quality.
If Welsh Tinplates are used, results will be satisfactory.

Applications for Welsh Tinplate, 1920.

Government backed Finance Corporation for Industry) sources enabled construction work to commence in 1947 on South Wales's second hot strip mill (the third in Wales as the mill at John Summers's Shotton Works in Deeside had come into operation in 1940). The site chosen for the project, one of coastal moorland at Margam, was adjacent to the existing Port Talbot and Margam Iron and Steel Works of Guest Keen and Baldwins which also underwent an extensive re-build as part of the modernisation scheme. Cold reduction and electrolytic tinning facilities were to be erected at Velindre (near Morriston) and Trostre (Llanelli) as adjuncts to the massive Margam and Abbey Works (as the new Port Talbot plant was then termed) from where a major portion of the output of the new 80" hot strip mill, commissioned in 1951, was destined for subsequent processing into tinplate.

A few years earlier, i.e. in 1948, the tinning process had undergone a revolutionary change when the first electrolytic tinning line in the United Kingdom was brought into operation at the Ebbw Vale Works of Richards Thomas and Baldwins Limited. The electrolytic process—again American developed technology—offered significant benefits in terms of labour productivity and especially in tin usage as only between 4 and 12 ounces of tin per box were consumed in the electrolytic process compared with the 20 to 24 ounces per box consumed in the traditional hot dipped method.

Whilst the decision to site the new hot strip mill at Port Talbot was not particularly controversial, strong views were expressed on the choice of site for the new cold reduction and electrolytic tinning plants. Several sites in South Wales had been looked at in detail; those rejected as unsuitable included the Machynys and Ynys sites at Llanelli, the Lower Swansea Valley, Jersey Marine (Swansea) and the one possibility in East Wales at Melingriffith, Cardiff. The two sites chosen, viz. Velindre, situated roughly mid-way between the traditional tinplate towns of Morriston and Gorseinon and that at Trostre, Llanelli, were well positioned to soak up the manpower consequentially displaced from the old type works. Work on clearing the Velindre site had already started when the Government of the day bowed to political pressure at both national and local levels and agreed that the industrial and social needs of the town of Llanelli were greater than those of North Swansea. And so site work came to a halt at Velindre when the men and machines engaged on the construction were transferred to a new site a few miles east of the town of Llanelli. After four years of work that began in August 1947, the plant and equipment at the Trostre Works, comprising a 5 stand cold reduction mill, two electrolytic tinning lines and associated equipment, was brought into operation; full production was achieved by 1954. Upon the completion of the major construction work at Trostre attention turned again to the Velindre site and by the summer of 1956 the five stand cold reduction mill, two electrolytic tinning lines and associated equipment installed at this works had been commissioned. The Steel Company of Wales Limited then had two 'new technology' plants in South West Wales compared with the one of Richard Thomas & Baldwins Ltd. at Ebbw Vale in South East Wales.[20]

To cater for subsequent increases in demand, additional electrolytic tinning capacity was installed later at all three works bringing the output potential of the Welsh tinplate industry, from 1968 under the sole control of the British Steel Coporation, to 1.2 million tons per annum from four electrolytic tinning lines at each of the three works.

The introduction of continuous strip rolling and electrolytic tinning emphasised the uneconomic working practices of old style hand mill plants. The number of these low productivity/high cost works in full operation (i.e. undertaking both rolling and tinning) fell from 76 in 1930 to 38 in 1950 and by 1961 all were closed in terms of all aspects of tinplate production. The tinning of plates by the hot dip method, however, had a slightly longer life-span than hand mill rolling as a consequence of the Elba Works and Kings Dock Works in Swansea and the Abercarn Works in north Gwent being operated as satellites to the Velindre and the Ebbw Vale Works to process cold reduced sheet into the small quantities of hot dipped tinplate required by certain customers for special applications. Trostre Works had its own 'in-house' hot dip tinning facility with nine pots but this again became a financial liability in the face of changing customer requirements and finally closed in 1978 after a gradual run-down in the number of pots in operation. The last link with the old process was severed in June 1982 when the only operating hot dip pot in the United Kingdom, located at the Metal Box Company's Eaglesbush Works, Neath, closed down.[21]

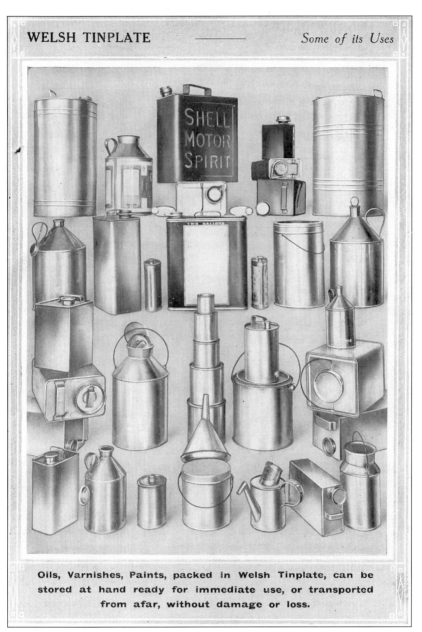

Oils, Varnishes, Paints, packed in Welsh Tinplate, can be stored at hand ready for immediate use, or transported from afar, without damage or loss.

Some further applications for tinplate, c. 1920.

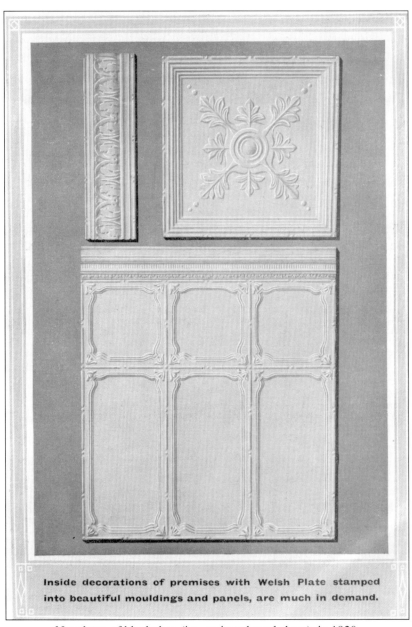

Inside decorations of premises with Welsh Plate stamped
into beautiful mouldings and panels, are much in demand.

Novel use of blackplate (i.e. untinned steel sheet), in 1920.

First beer cans made in Britain for Felinfoel Brewery, Llanelli, c. 1935.

Beer cans in 1980.

NOTES

[1] Ess, T.J., (Ed), *The Modern Strip Mill* (Published by the Associated of Iron and Steel Engineers [U.S.A.], 1941).

[2] Cound, S.R., 'How to Improve Welsh Tinplate Rolling Mill Practice' (*Proc. of South Wales Institute of Engineers,* 13th April 1915).

[3] Minchinton, W., *The British Tinplate Industry: A. History.*

[4] Thomas, H. Spence, *Report in the Western Mail Trade Supplement of 7th January 1935.*

[5] Brooke, E. H., op. cit.

[6] Ibid.

[7] Ibid.

[8] Minchinton W., op. cit.

[9] Williams, J., 'How to Improve Welsh Tinplate Rolling Mill Practice' (*Proc. of South Wales Institute of Engineers,* 13th April 1915).

[10] 'The Dragon', August 1967 and Reader, W.J., *Metal Box—A History.*

[11] Ess, T.J. (Ed.), ibid.

[12] Hogan, William T., *Economic History of the Iron and Steel Industry in the United States. Vol. 3 Parts IV and V.* (D.C. Heath & Co. Lexington Mass).

[13] Minchinton, W., op. cit.

[14] Tolliday, S.W., *Industry, Finance and the State: An Analysis of the British Steel Industry in the Inter-War Years* (Unpublished Ph.D. Thesis, Cambridge, 1979).

[15] Ibid.

[16] Warren, Kenneth, *The British Iron and Steel Sheet Industry since 1840* (G. Bell & Sons, London, 1970).

[17] Ibid.

[18] Papers in Authori's Collection.

[19] Brooke, E.H., op. cit.

[20] British Steel plc., Archives: *The Steel Company of Wales Ltd.*

[21] *South Wales Evening Post,* 20th June 1982.

4. PROCESS DEVELOPMENTS AND MANUFACTURING PROCEDURES

> Iron is the metal which is most easily destroyed, it lies open to the weakest dissolvents, even common water attacks it with success. Sometimes a little water is sufficient to destroy the finest parts of the best polished works: in order to protect that which its use is exposed to the action of water, it has been usual to cover it with different coatings, some are oiled, the most precious are gilded, some are bronzed—it is thought of covering the commonest with tin.

The above translation of a report written in 1725 by Rene-Antoine Ferchault de Reaumur, a French metallurgist, refers to the protective qualities of tin when applied as a coating to iron.[1]

The art of manufacturing 'tinned plate' has undergone many changes since first practised by the mid Europeans in the fourteenth century. Thereafter, the technology employed has advanced from being primitive, requiring nothing more than crude equipment and the practised skills of the work-people, to the sophisticated systems of today where process control is achieved by electronic means and the manual dexterity of the workmen by and large, has been replaced by automated mechanisms requiring a new kind of expertise.

These changes reflect the tinplate makers pursuit of higher outputs, greater productivity, improved quality and lower costs; they have not in any way altered the basic physical procedures involved in tinplate manufacture since first developed in the fourteenth century. In essence these are:—

(a) the production of the iron (or as later steel) base

(b) the flattening of the iron or steel base into sheet form

(c) the application of a coating of tin onto the flattened sheet. Similarly, the principal technical developments associated with tinplate making fall into the following three distinct phases, albeit with a degree of overlap between each:

—14th Century to early 18th Century—production of iron sheet under the forging hammer with hand pickling, tinning and cleaning

—early 18th Century to early 20th Century—hot rolling in pack form with batch pickling and single sheet tinning

—from early 20th Century to present—rolling in strip form with electrolytic tinning.

63

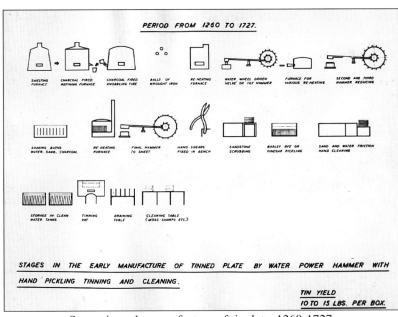

Stages in early manufacture of tinplate, 1260-1727.

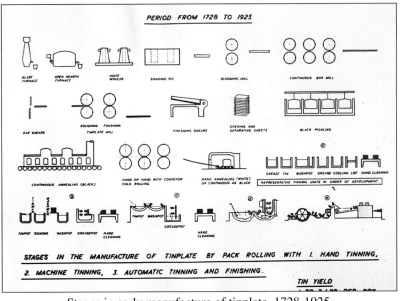

Stages in early manufacture of tinplate, 1728-1925.

Fundamentally, the methods employed in converting iron from its mineral state to a usable product (i.e. by smelting ore in a furnace) are the same now as they were when man, more by accident than design, first discovered the art some three thousand years ago.

Iron ore, the raw material of iron smelting, and a suitable flux (limestone, for example) are both charged into a furnace into which a fuel has been placed and ignited. A blast of air directed onto the fuel raises the temperature within the furnace to a level at which the iron within the ore changes into a molten state. The breaching of the hearth of the furnace—a procedure known as 'tapping'—frees the molten iron. Until the beginning of this century the molten iron was allowed to run into furrows of sand known as 'sows' and 'pigs'—hence the term 'pig iron'—positioned at the front of the furnace. Here they were allowed to cool and solidify before being subjected to further processing. Nowadays, the iron is retained in its molten state for a further refinement stage during which most of the remaining impurities are removed and the iron becomes steel. Of course, contemporary process control techniques ensure that the quality of the product is vastly superior to that obtained from the earliest furnaces, capable of producing no more than a few pounds of iron per charge in comparison with the forty thousand tonnes per week obtainable from a single modern blast furnace.

Charcoal, created by the controlled carbonisation of wood, was the fuel first used to generate the heat for the smelting process. Charcoal was produced by a slow, labour intensive operation, wasteful of natural resources (a sizeable area of woodland was needed to support a single furnace) and therefore was a high cost fuel. Also, the brittleness of charcoal prevented furnace charges from being maximised; too much ore and limestone in the charge fractured and compressed the fuel and by doing reduced the degree of penetration of the air blast through the furnace bottom to the top. If this happened the temperature at which the smelting process took place (1150°C and above) could not be achieved.

Pioneering work undertaken by Abraham Darby and his son at Coalbrookdale, Shropshire, in the first half of the eighteenth century enabled iron smelters to use coke (i.e. de-carbonised coal) in their furnaces. The cost effectiveness of coke in comparison with charcoal and the benefits of higher furnace outputs were quickly appreciated by eighteenth century iron makers. New iron works, such as those at

Merthyr, Dowlais, Tredegar and Blaenavon in South Wales, sprang up on the coalfields, utilising the indigenous fuel.

However, the use of a mineral fuel was not entirely beneficial to the tinplate maker as iron produced in a coke smelting furnace had a high sulphur content and this, in the early days, adversely affected the quality of the finished tinplate. Although acceptable as the base material for the standard product, iron with a high sulphur content was unsuitable for the manufacture of the best quality tinplate. A means of reducing the level of the sulphur was needed if coke iron was to be a complete success with the tinplate makers. The solution lay with the use of charcoal, not coke, in the immediate stage of sheet iron manufacture i.e. that between the production of pig or cast iron in the blast furnaces and the forging/rolling of the iron into sheet form.

Whilst pig iron is satisfacory for the manufacture of castings, where further working of the metal is unnecessary, its brittleness, caused by a 2% to 4% carbon content, rendered it incapable of being worked either under the forging hammer or in the rolling mill. Further processing was necessary to remove most of the remaining carbon and transform the cast iron into the more malleable 'wrought iron'. Initially this was achieved by submitting the pig iron to a 'finery' and a 'chafery'. The procedures involved in this process were described in a paper prepared by Henry Powle Esq. and printed in the *Philosophical Transactions* for 1676:

> From these furnaces (blast furnaces) they bring their sows and pigs of iron to their forges. They are of two sorts, though standing together under the same roof: one they call their Finery and the other the Chafery. Both of them are open hearths, on which they place great heaps of charcoal, and behind them bellows, like those of the furnaces, but nothing near so large. Into the Finery they first put their pigs of iron, placing three or four of them together behind the fire with a little of one end thrust into it. When softening, by degrees, they stir and work them with long bars of iron, till the metal runs together into a round mass or lump, which they call a half bloom. This they take out, and giving it a few strokes with their sledges, they carry it to a great weighty hammer, raised likewise by the motion of a water wheel, where applying it dextrously to the blows, they presently beat it out into a thick, short square. This they put into the Chafery, and heating it red hot, they work it out under

the same hammer, till it comes into the shape of a bar in the middle with two square knobs in the ends. Last of all they give it other heatings in the Chafery, and more workings under the hammer till they have brought their iron into bars several shapes and sizes, in which fashion they expose them for sale.[2]

In both the finery and the chafery, charcoal was the only fuel used. The basic construction of the finery and chafery furnaces (they were but simple hearths into which the fuel and pig iron were simultaneously charged) allowed the pig iron to come into direct contact with the furnace fuel. Because of the direct contact, the iron became contaminated through its absorption of impurities from within the charcoal. Whilst iron produced via the finery and chafery was used for tinplate manufacture, again it was not of a quality ideally suited to the needs of the tinplate makers.

In 1784 a patent taken out by Henry Cort described a new type of furnace known as the 'reverberatory furnace'. The concept employed by Cort was that the fuel and the charge of pig iron should be kept in separate but adjacent chambers with only the flame or the heat given off by the fuel having contact with the charge. Consequently, the opportunities for the transference of impurities from the fuel to the iron were minimised. This development meant that the iron smelters could use mineral fuel in place of the more expensive charcoal with a greater degree of confidence over the quality of their iron. Cort's concept, subsequently improved by Samuel Rogers of Nant-y-Glo and Joseph Hall of Tipton, Staffs.,[3] was known as 'puddling' because of the stirring action required of the furnace operators. Generally two men—a Puddler and his Assistant—were employed to work a single furnace and the following description of the process can give but a hint of the physical exertion required of them in conditions of extreme heat.

Each charge consisted of about 4 hundred weights of pig iron pieces. The Assistant placed the pieces on the end of a long rod (or peel) held by the Puddler who then proceeded to carefully distribute each piece around the inside of the furnace. With the charge 'in situ' the furnace door was closed and sealed with sand by the Assistant who also made up the fire in the adjoining compartment. Approximately half an hour after charging, the iron had reached a viscous state and was ready for the constant working or stirring by, in turns, the Puddler and his Assistant using an iron rod called a rabble.

Puddling furnace, c. 1890.

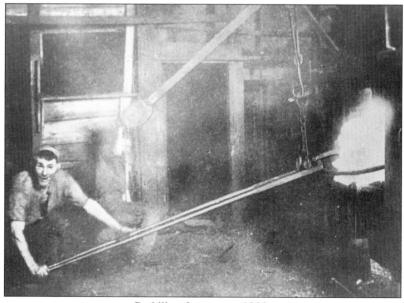
Puddling furnace, c. 1900.

The stirring process continued for a further one and a half to two hours, the furnace operators alternatively exposing themselves to the intense heat of the furnace until the metal was said to have 'come to nature' i.e. when formed into small pellets. The slag and cinder residues were then run off into pots positioned in front of the furnace. When 'further in nature' the pellets agglomerated into a pasty mass that could be split into four to six balls, each weighing between eighty and ninety pounds. These were removed from the furnace and presented individually to the forge hammers for flattening into sheet. During the forging stage, in one of a series of re-heatings prior to each hammering, the opportunity was taken to further reduce the sulphur content of the iron by roasting the charge on a bed of charcoal—a procedure that enhanced the quality of the product.

The relationship between tinplate making and forging operations is further evidenced by reference to the Llwydarth Tinplate Works situated at Maesteg, Mid Glamorgan. The *Central Glamorgan Gazette* on 14th June 1872 reported the opening of a forge at the Works measuring 180 feet by 143 feet, providing employment for a further 70 men in addition to the 130 employed in the two-mill tin works (a third mill was to be added shortly). The new forge consisted of six puddling and two balling and re-heating furnace. The waste heat of the furnaces was said to have been conducted under four large boilers to generate steam for powering the machinery in the tin mills and in the forge 'by which scheme there is a very great saving of coal". Machinery installed in the forge comprised a large double-action steam hammer, a 20 inch horizontal condensing engine for driving the bar rolls together with a blowing apparatus for the manufacture of charcoal bars and associated equipment.

By 1872 the number of puddling furnaces in operation in South Wales approached 1,200 out of the 7,300[4] installed throughout the length and breadth of the United Kingdom and although the use of charcoal in the tinplate manufacturing process had ceased by the end of the nineteenth century, its demise being hastened by the successful application of steel (i.e. low carbon iron) to tinplate making in 1876, the term 'charcoal tinplate' continued in use within the trade up to the time of the passing of the hand mills. Charcoal tinplate, whilst in terms of its manufacture having no connection at all with the use of charcoal as a fuel from the mid-nineteenth century onwards, distinguished the best quality tinplate from 'coke' or standard quality tinplate.

Helve or Tilt Hammer, driven by water.

The next stage in the process was the conversion of the balls of wrought iron into sheet form in the forge. Up to and including the seventeenth century the 'helves' or tilt hammers of the forges, relying on water as their power source, were the only available means of obtaining a reasonably flat and thin sheet of iron. The sequence of operations consisted of a series of heatings and hammerings, the forgeman and his assistant dextrously transferring the ball of iron between the furnace and the hammer before submitting it, transformed into several sheets, to the tinning room for the final stages of the process.

In the tinning department (or to use its more familiar name within the trade 'the tin house') the sheets were subjected to several distinct operations before finally emerging as 'tinned plate'. The procedures followed in manufacturing tinplate in the period before the advent of rolling are comprehensively documented in a report by M. Diderot published in 1750 in the *Encyclopedie ou Dictionnaire Raisonne des Sciences, des Arts et des Metiers par une Societe de Gens de Lettres*.[5] The report, translated below, describes tinplate making at the Mansvaux

70

Manufacture of bar iron—Mansvaux Works, France, 1714.

Works (established 1714) in the Alsace Region of France. Undoubtedly, the processes outlined by Diderot are comparable with those employed in the early Welsh works except, of course, that in Wales the final reduction in the thickness of the sheet to the gauge required before the application of the tin coating would have been achieved by passing the bar iron through a set of powered rollers. In the absence of any contemporary report on the manufacturing procedures of the Welsh tinplate makers, Diderot's detailed statement is a valuable piece of evidence.

The iron is brought to the works in little bars, the best is that which is ductile and soft, and which forges well when cold, but it is not essential that the iron should have these qualities in excess.

The bars are heated in the furnace, and they are then slightly hammered out on an anvil. Afterwards they are placed under the large hammer and cut into pieces.

This produces two sheets of tin-plates which are first heated until they sparkle violently in the forge and then roughly reheated, before being hammered a third time and finally placed again under the same large hammer until they are almost double their first dimensions. After this they are doubled up according to their length.

Next they are dipped in water which contains a sandy earth, to which it is well to add some charcoal dust; the effect of this immersion is to prevent adhesion.

When a large quantity of these doubled sheets has been prepared, each is carried to the furnace, where it is placed vertically side by side on its edge on two bars of iron, which support several sheets, forming a pile varying in size according to their thickness.

A lever of iron, which can be raised or lowered according to circumstances, serves to hold this bundle tight whilst being surrounded by very large pieces of charcoal, which are ignited.

When he considers that the bundle is sufficiently heated, a workman takes a packet of forty of these double sheets and places them under the hammer. The second hammer is larger than the first, it weights 700 lbs and is not so sharp. Here the packet is beaten until the sheets have acquired their proper dimensions and it may be noticed that the outside sheets, namely, those which touch the anvil and the hammer, are not stretched so much as those contained within them, for the inside sheets retain their heat the longest, the outside sheets require more heat and more hammering.

After this first operation they place between the sheets those which in the previous operation had not been sufficiently stretched; thus they perform the same operations on all the packets.

The intermixed packet is then placed on the fire and heated again. When sufficiently heated the plates are taken out of the fire in packets of about 100 sheets each. These packets are divided into two equal parts and arranged in such a manner that those which were formerly on the top are placed beneath.

They are carried in this state to the big hammer and beaten. More waste sheets are intermixed, and taken to the fire. After heating, each packet is divided into two parts as before and are again turned upside down and hammered for the third time before being cut to size by the same workmen.

For this purpose he makes use of a pair of shears and a measure which determines the length of the sheet, each sheet is cut separately. When each sheet is cut and squared, an operation in

Manufacture of sheets from bar iron by repeated heating and hammering—
Mansvaux Works, France, 1714.

which the doubled sheet is divided into two, the shears removing
the bend, all the sheets are placed in piles on two thick flat bars of
red-hot iron positioned on the ground. The piles are closed by the
placing of one or two thick bars of flat iron above them. Whilst the
sheets of one pile are being worked the packet which is to follow
advances to the stage of being squared. But in the heating which
immediately precedes the squaring operation, each packet is divided
into two and placed between these two equal portions of unsquared
sheets is a certain quantity of squared sheets; the workmen carry the
whole to the big hammers where by a further hammering the
squared sheets receive their last polish. After this operation the
squared sheets go to the cellar and the unsquared sheets to the
shears.

Of the sheets which are ready for the cellar those which are large
and imperfect are put aside to be sold as sheet iron, whilst the others
are destined to be made into tin plates. Those to be made into tin

plates are scrubbed with sandstone before transfer to the cellar or cave where they are put in vats of sour water, that is to say, in a mixture of water and barley meal or rye which is excited to acid fermentation by the action of great heat created and kept by the furnace. Here, the smell is very strong and the heat most unpleasant.

This is done to clean the sheets, that is to say, to remove the scale of the forge which still covers them.

The sheets remain for seventy-two fours in this water, and are turned from time to time. They are taken out and given to the women who rub them with sand and water, using a cork and a rag.

After scouring, the sheets are put in water to protect them from the red rust, i.e. the fine rust which forms upon them. From the water they pass to the tin-house.

The tinning apparatus consists of a cauldron of cast iron placed in the middle of a kind of table with plates of iron slightly included towards the cauldron and properly connected with it.

This cauldron is much deeper than the width of the sheet, which is always plunged in vertically and never on the surface. It contains 1500 to 2000kilos of tin. In the masonry which supports the cauldron is fixed a stove like a baker's of which the chimney is above the door and which has no opening alongside but is on the opposite side to the tinman. This stove is heated with wood.

The tinman commences his work at six in the morning; at ten o'clock on the previous night he placed his tin to melt in the furnace. When the tin melts it will be left for six hours in a state of fusion, before the 'secret' is introduced.

No-one knows exactly what this mystery is, but it is assumed that it is copper, and this supposition is founded on the fact that the metal which is mixed should assist in the coating, and copper would have that quality because it is of a medium fusibility between iron and tin.

The tin is melted under a coating of grease from four to five inches in thickness, because molten tin calcines readily when it is in fusion and exposed to the air. This precaution prevents such exposure, and perhaps even reduces some small portion of the tin which has already been calcined. This is a secret of which the manufacturers of tinned articles are very well aware.

From six o'clock in the morning, when the tin is at a proper heat (for when it is not hot enough it will not stick to the iron, and when

74

The tinning process at the Mansvaux Works, 1714.

it is too hot the coating is thin and unequal) they begin to work. They dip in the tin pot the sheets that have been taken out of the water, the workman throwing them in altogether on their sides without troubling himself to separate them, and subsequently they are nearly all taken out together. This first operation having been performed on all the sheets the workman takes a part of them, which he plunges altogether into his molten tin, turning and re-turning them in every direction, dividing and sub-dividing his packet without taking them out of the cauldron. He then takes them one by one and dips them separately in a chamber separated by a plate of iron which forms a partition in the tin-pot, He takes them from the large cauldron to plunge them one by one in this division. Having done this he puts them to drain on two small bars of iron placed parallel with each other and on their edges between small spikes of iron fixed perpendicularly. The sheets are placed upon the parallel bars of iron which support them and between the vertical bars which keep them upright.

A little girl takes each sheet from out of this drainer, and if there are any little spots that have not taken the tin she scrapes them briskly with a kind of scraper and puts them on one side, from whence they are returned to the tinning.

As to those which are perfect they are distributed to girls who, with sawdust and moss, rub them a long time to get the grease off. After that it is necessary to remove a kind of list which is formed on one side of the sheet when it is put in the drainer. To accomplish this they dip the lower edge or border very carefully in molten tin specially taking care that the sheet is not dipped either too long or too short a time, otherwise the last coating in flowing might melt off the other and the sheet would remain black and imperfect.

After this immersion a workman rubs the plates briskly on both sides with moss, taking off the superfluous tin and the sheets are finished.

They make sheets of different widths, lengths, and thicknesses; the workmen say that the profit is immense.

It is evident from the description that great care was taken to produce a product of a quality acceptable to the tinsmiths. However, irrespective of the skill and conscientiousness of the forgeman, the action of the helve on the iron bar inevitably produced sheets of uneven thickness and poor surface quality. In particular, the grain imparted in the iron during the preceding smelting and casting processes to a large extent was destroyed by the action of the forge hammer, a defect which caused splits and cracks to open up on the surface of the tinned sheet when being formed by the tinsmith into the finished article. Moreover, the undulating surface of the hammered sheet did not fully meet the demands of the skilled tinsmiths who by using their craftsmanship sought to produce articles with a smooth, highly reflective finish.

The means by the which these problems were overcome was simple but effective. The passing of the heated 'thick iron' (i.e. iron bars forged to a thickness varying between ½" and 1") through a pair of polished cast iron rolls not only improved sheet flatness but also reduced production costs by both speeding up the manufacturing process and improving the surface quality of the product.

The evolution of the techniques involved in the rolling of metals into the shape or form required is a fascinating study in itself. At the end of the fifteenth century, Leonardo da Vinci designed a mill for

Water-powered tilt hammer used for hammering iron into thin sheets before the introduction of rolling. German wood-cut, c. 1700.

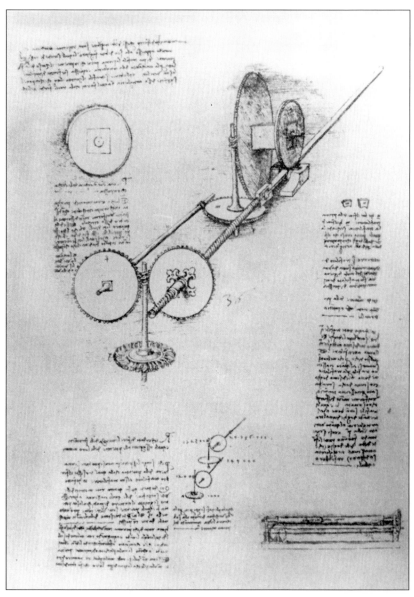

Leonardo da Vinci's sketch of machine to roll lead for stained-glass windows.

rolling window leads and in seeking to further the application of the concept sketched a plan of a mill for rolling wide strips of soft metal which he claimed 'can be used for organ pipes or metal rooftiles'.[6] In 1553 a Frenchman named Brulier passed gold and silver discs between a pair of rolls for the dual purpose of producing an evenness of thickness and imparting a polished surface on them before they were stamped into coins.[7]

In 1615 a mill to roll and impart the curve on sheets of lead or pewter destined to become organ pipes was developed by De Caus.[8] In De Caus' mill the screwdown mechanism by which the gap between the rolls was reduced gradually to enable thin sheets to be produced can be seen clearly in the illustration. Note also the hand operation with a direct drive to the top roll.

The ingenuity of Branca, an Italian engineer, as portrayed in his 1629 mill has to be admired.[9] Whether or not the utilisation of hot air currents from a blacksmith's forge as a power source was successful cannot be ascertained but as a concept it certainly was novel. If it ever became reality the low level of power obtainable from hot air currents,

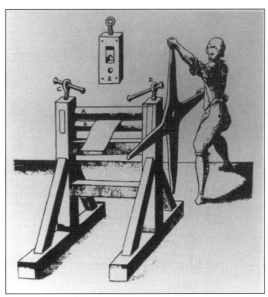

Set of rolls used to run out flat sheets of lead for fabrication into organ pipes (illustration from *Les Raisons des Forces Movantes* by Soloman De Caus [printed in France in 1615]).

when combined with the complex system of gearing for the transference of the drive to the rolls, would have restricted the scope of the mill to the working of thin, soft metals such as lead or copper. Mills for slitting (i.e. cutting) iron were in use before the end of the sixteenth century. In all probability the first British slitting mill was the one reported as operating in Dartford, Kent in 1590.

As indicated earlier, the rolling of bar iron into sheets for the subsequent application of a coating of tin was a technique initiated in Britain by the Hanbury family at their Pontypool Works some time between the years 1680 and 1720. Whilst this was an event of paramount important for the tinplate trade, the Hanburys cannot be accredited with having first thought of producing various shapes out of bar iron by passing it between a pair of rollers. The small amount of evidence available to us today suggests that the technique may have originated in the Midlands around the year 1680. Dr. Robert Plot's *Natural History of Staffordshire* (published in 1686) states that forged bars were cut into short lengths and 'then brought singly to the rollers, by which they are drawn even and to a greater length before being passed through the cutters'.[10] This is one of the first references to a rolling mill in use in the iron trade, although in this case it was used for the production of rods.

With their roots set in Midlands soil, the Hanbury family probably had contacts in the area and information about this development may have passed through these to the Pontypool iron makers who, realising its potential, soon introduced the practice at their establishment. Edward Llwyd, a Welsh traveller and writer, confirms the existence of a rolling mill at Pontypool in his 1697 report prepared following a visit to the works. In the report Llwyd gives the following fairly detailed account of the rolling procedures introduced at Pontypool:

They cut their common iron bars into pieces of about two foot long and heating them glowing hot, place them betwixt these iron rollers, not across, but their ends lying the same way as the ends of the rollers. The rollers (moved with water) drive out these bars to such thin plates that their breadth, which was about four inches, becomes their length, being extended to about four feet, and what was before the length of the bars is now the breadth of the plates. With these plates he makes furnaces, pots, kettles, saucepans etc. These he can afford at a very cheap rate (about the third part of what is usual).[11]

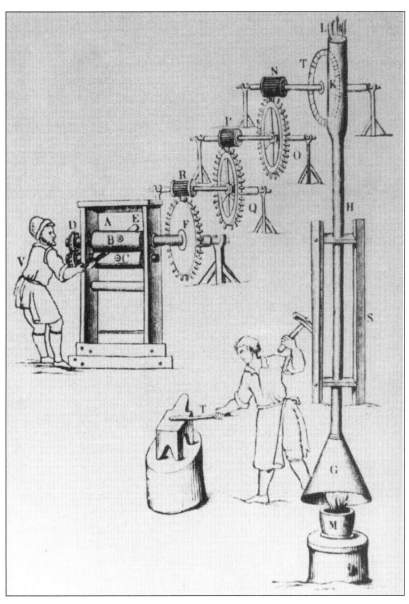

Branca's Mill, 1829.

Further and perhaps more descriptive evidence of iron rolling at Pontypool is to be found in a manuscript entitled 'Resa Genom England' written in the early part of the eighteenth century by R.R. Angerstein, a Swedish traveller and writer.[12] Angerstein's sketches of the equipment installed at both the Pontypool and the Woolard, Somerset Works, clearly depict the earliest method of mill construction. If Angerstein's sketches and Llwyd's statement are accurate descriptions of what they observed, the drive induced by water flowing over the wheels was applied to both top and bottom rolls; crude screw down gear enabled pressure to be exerted through the roll housings to the necks of the single pair of rolls. The two mills at Pontypool, each containing rolls of dimensions 14 inches in length and 11 to 12 inches in diameter, were worked by two teams of three men. Other illustrations in the Angerstein manuscript are of the re-heat furnace (by which the iron bars were heated before rolling) and the tinning pot installed at the Pontypool Works.

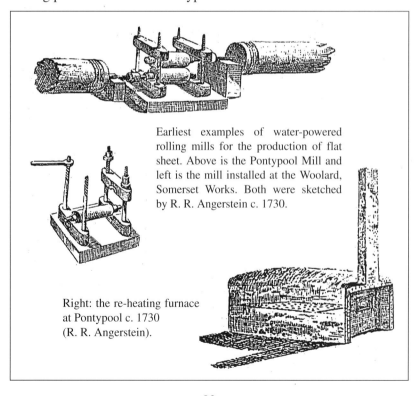

Earliest examples of water-powered rolling mills for the production of flat sheet. Above is the Pontypool Mill and left is the mill installed at the Woolard, Somerset Works. Both were sketched by R. R. Angerstein c. 1730.

Right: the re-heating furnace at Pontypool c. 1730 (R. R. Angerstein).

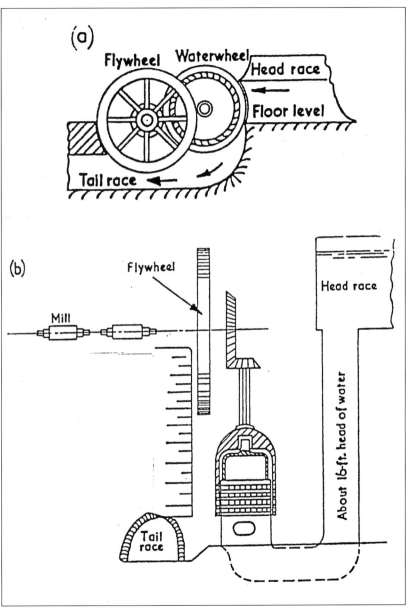

Types of water wheels used in tinplate trade: (a) breast type (sectional view);
(b) over-shot wheel (plan).

Water, exclusively, was the earliest source of power utilised by tinplate manufactures—a factor restricting the choice of sites available for tinplate works to those adjacent to fast-flowing rivers or streams. Insufficient flow rate could be countered by the construction of weirs to hold back a quantity of water for subsequent discharge in a controlled manner through leets or channels, which also served to divert the stream onto the wheel; the higher the elevation of the flume discharge onto the wheel, the greater the force of the water. Wheel design fell into four basic categories viz. over-shot, under-shot, breast or Pelton, each one suiting the physical conditions of the locality and the layout of the works but with the breast type evidently being favoured most by tinplate makers.[13] Water flowing onto the top of the wheel became trapped in the wheel laths and after imparting its power discharged itself into the tail race. From this simple apparatus was later developed the more sophisticated vertical and horizontal water turbine similar to the one installed in the Melingriffith Works, Cardiff.[14] Despite the advent of steam and electricity as alternatives, water continued to be used as an important power source in a number of works until well into the twentieth century.[15]

Water-wheel at the Edlogan Works (exterior new).

Water-wheel at the Edlogan Works (interior view).

The introduction of the rolling mill powered by water increased by a considerable degree the pace at which bar iron was transformed into sheet. Four men were capable of producing an average of one ton of plates in twelve hours operating a rolling mill compared with the meagre 100 lbs (maximum) achievable by the same number of men working the tilt hammer over an equivalent period of time. Nonetheless, the use of water brought its own problems. In periods of drought or when ice constrained the rate of flow production was brought to a standstill and trade reports indicate that during periods of particularly severe drought or frost some mills were unable to operate for more than forty weeks in the year.

No such problems existed with machinery—generated energy sources such as steam or electricity. From two drawings of the 'Lower Redbrook Tin Mill' dated 1798 and 1799 it would appear that by the close of the eighteenth century the 'mill' was in fact a pair of matching mills (i.e. the roughing mill and the finishing mill) positioned alongside each other. Both mills contained rolls of 14 inches in diameter by 18 inches long.[16] The mill housings consisted of cast iron uprights resting on a pillow block and capped by a similar block, again made of cast iron. Also discernible from the drawings is the method of drive which in the case of the Redbrook Mill was applied to both the top and the bottom rolls. However, the significant feature of the drawings is the steam engine depicted attached to the mill on the 1798 plan. The idea behind the installation of the engine may have been the provision of a supplementary source of power at times when the water flow rate was inadequate. Whether or not the concept was tested in practice cannot be confirmed and because of the lack of further evidence it must be assumed that the engine shown in the plan was incapable of generating sufficient power to force the bar through the rolls and reduce its thickness without the mill stalling i.e. being brought to a halt.

Until recently it was widely accepted that steam powered tinplate mills were first introduced at the Landore Works, Swanse in 1851. This assumption, based on statements by E.H. Brooke in his *Chronology of the Tinplate Works of Great Britain*, has been brought into question by a relatively recent comprehensive survey of the archival material from the Neath Abbey Ironworks Company. Amongst the extant drawings of the long defunct ironworks are several relating to steam engines for tinplate works pre-dating the Landore development. In the collection are drawings for a rotative beam engine for driving rolling mills at an unspecified location dated 1825, an 1828 table engine of 38 h.p. for the Margam Tinplate Works and a 21 inches by 6 feet rotative beam engine for the Aberdulais (near Neath) Tinplate Works of around 1842. Evidently, therefore, steam driven mills were in operation at least twenty-five years earlier than hitherto believed.[17]

Throughout the second half of the nineteenth century tinplate manufacturers increasingly turned to using steam engines to power their mills and by 1886 only 46 out of 386 mills operating within the trade continued to rely on water for their motive power.[18] With the advent of the steam engine the concept of connecting the mill drive to a massive fly-wheel increased in use. Soon fly-wheels were universal features of tinplate works. Dwarfing the mills they served, the cast iron fly-wheels, some having a diameter of 36 feet and weight of 130 tons, were introduced to lessen the risk of the mill stalling when the bar iron was presented to the rolls. When in motion, the continuously spinning fly-wheel increased the energy and power within the mill, enabling thin elongated sheets to be produced from thick iron or steel

86

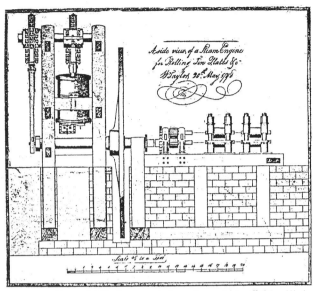

Lower Redbrook (Gwent) Works—end elevation of 'double' mill depicting atmospheric steam engine, dated 1798.

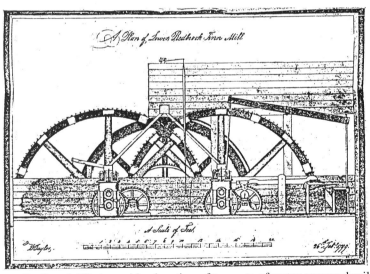

Lower Redbrook Works—side elevation of two sets of water-powered mills, dated 1799.

enabling thin elongated sheets to be produced from thick iron or steel bars of up to one inch in thickness.

The early steam-driven beam engines were at or near to maximum load working two pairs of mills housing small diameter rolls but by 1880 larger and more sophisticated engines were capable of powering up to four pairs of mills each. The final stage, with six pairs of mills housing 26 inches diameter rolls, serviced by engines of about 1500 h.p. similar to that installed at the St. Davids (Loughor) Tinplate Works, began soon after the turn of the century. The type and manufacture of tinplate works' steam engines varied not only from works to works but also within individual establishments where the separate functions, i.e. hot rolling and cold rolling, and the layout of the plant and equipment called for engines of specific capabilities and design. The Baglan Bay Tinplate Company, for example, installed at its Briton Ferry works engines made by Edwin Foden of Sandbach and by Galloways of Manchester. Both Daniel Adamson and Company and Cole, Merchant and Morley supplied engines to the St. David's

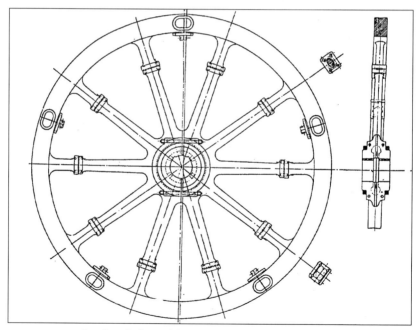

Sectional view of flywheel attached to mill drive:
diameter = 36 feet; weight = 120 tons.

Works at Loughor whilst the famous Hick, Hargreaves & Company's engines operated within the Abercarn Works and that of John Player and Son at Clydach in the Swansea Valley.[19] The introduction of steam power and in 1905 electricity (initially, according to E.H. Brooke, at the Elba Works, Swansea) to drive the mills raised the output potential of a mill crew of six men working an eight hours shift to three and a half tons.

Although the Welsh tinplate makers were not entirely dilatory in introducing firstly steam engines and later electric motors to power their mills, both the design of a tinplate hand mill and the techniques employed in the production of a flat sheet changed little over the two centuries following the Capel Hanbury's pioneering work at Pontypool. From about 1890 onwards, when steel gained in prominence over iron as the base material, the 'Pack' or 'Hand' Mill method of tinplate production was in common use throughout the industry until overtaken by the Continuous Strip Mill. The manufacturing procedure commenced with the receipt at the tinworks of the bar iron (or 'tin bar' as it was better known) produced at the steelworks. The bars, usually between 15 and 20 feet in length by 9 inches wide and between 3/8 inch and 7/8 inch in thickness, were first sheared by a Bar Cutter and his Assistant into shorter lengths of about 20 inches, each corresponding to the required width of the finished sheet of blackplate (the term used to identify the sheets up to the stage in the process when the tin coating was applied after which it became tinplate) with an allowance for scrap.

After cutting, between thirty and forty bars were charged into the hot mill furnace—a reverberatory type furnace fired by coal although in later years both oil and gas were used as fuels, improving both performance and employees' working conditions. Two furnaces—the roughing furnace which heated the bar from cold and the finishing furnace for the final stages of the rolling process—were erected side-by-side to service one double mill. In the early days much emphasis was laid on the skill of a furnaceman to bring the heat of his furnace and the bars placed therein to the optimum temperature (between 750 and 800 degrees centigrade) for hot rolling.

The process of hot rolling reduced the thickness of the bar whilst at the same time extending it to a length roughly commensurate with the ordered size of the finished tinplate but with appropriate allowances for the offcuts generated when the sheet was later sheared to the exact

Steam engine at Lydney Works, Glos. Built by Millbrook Engineering Company, Landore, Swansea. Erected in 1888 and dismantled in 1956.

400 h.p. electric motor built by the Power Plant Co. Ltd., of West Drayton, and installed at Lydney Works, Glos. in 1956 to replace steam engine.

dimensions. Basically, each mill consisted of a pair of rolls in vertical sequence within a housing. The gap between the rolls through which the bar iron passed was adjustable by the Rollerman (the senior man in the mill crew) operating a lever mechanism which activated screws positioned in the mill housings, increasing or reducing as the case may be, the pressure on the necks (i.e. the ends of the roll machined to a smaller diameter than the roll body which came into contact with the sheet) of the upper roll.

The bars, when sufficiently 'soaked' (i.e. heated to c. 800°C), were withdrawn from the furnace by the Furnaceman using a pair of tongs, boshed in cold water to remove scale and dirt and passed a few feet along a steel plated floor to the mill Rollerman who, again with the aid of a pair of tongs, lifted the bars individually and presented them to the nip of the rolls. As each bar emerged from the rolls, having been reduced a little in thickness, it was caught and passed back over the top of the upper roll by the Behinder, positioned at the back of the mill, to the Rollerman who in the meantime would have submitted a second bar to the rolls. This sequence of heating and rolling was repeated a second time after which the bars became thick plates of about 30 inches in length called, at this stage, 'singles'.

Of the three methods of rolling plates from bar termed three-part, four-part and five-part (or Welsh) systems, the latter was by far the most popular within the trade. Each system gained its name from the number of times a bar needed to be passed through both mills before it acquired the correct gauge and length. In the five-part system the 'long single' sheet obtained after two passes was 'doubled', i.e. folded in two, by the Doubler working alongside a combined squeezer and crocodile shears. Using his tongs, the Doubler brought the sheet to the floor, bent it back across its width and started the centre fold by means of foot pressure. The feet of the Doubler were always protected by thick clogs as the sheet was still hot at this stage. The fold was completed by the Doubler placing the partly folded end of the sheet under a mechanically (or, as later, electrically) operated squeezer. The sheets were known as 'doubles' at this stage but were changed into 'fours' and 'eights' by a further three passes (making five in all) through the furnaces and mills—a folding operation following each pass. Scrap, including the curl of the folded sheets, was sheared off at appropriate stages in the procedure. The end result was two packs of

Unloading of steel bar received from steelworks.

Cutting steel bar to size prior to Hot Rolling.

92

rolled blackplates, each consisting of eight individual plates. The rolling of sheets in the old hand mills was a precise art which depended greatly on the individual skill and judgement of the Roller and his crew. The human element entered into the production of rolled sheets in the hand mill to a far greater extent than in most other steel based products.

The pressure exerted on the 'packed' sheets during rolling caused them to adhere to each other and separation of the individual sheets was necessary before their submission to the pickling department for the next stage in the process. The opening of the 'stickers', as the plates which had stuck together were called, was performed by women—the Openers. Each Opener held a pack of sheets edgewise and struck the corner of the outer plate in the pack with the palm of the hand, protected by a leather glove into which had been sewn a piece of lead. With the corner bent outwards as a result of the strike, the outside 'sticker' could be freed from the rest of the pack by an outwards sweep of the arm. Sheets that sometimes resisted separation by hand were forced apart by the Opener using a metal cleaver—a long-bladed machete-like instrument.

After the separation of each sheet from the pack, those found to be defective were discarded and the remaining good quality ones 'pickled' in a mild acid solution. This removed the film of iron oxide (scale) that had accumulated on the surface during the process of rolling. In the making of tinplate by the hand mill method each sheet was pickled twice, the first pickling following hot rolling was termed 'black pickling' to distinguish it from the second or 'white' pickling treatment after cold rolling.

As indicated by Diderot's eighteenth century description, in the early days the removal of forging scale from the plates was achieved by their immersion in a mixture of water and barley meal or rye. Soon after the middle of the century the pickling solution consisted of a mixture of spirits of salt or 'marine' acid and water in the proportions of two pints of acid to three gallons of water but in 1829 Thomas Morgan of the Melingriffith Works, Cardiff, secured the patent for a pickling solution based on sulphuric acid that quickly gained universal acceptance with the trade.[20]

General view of Hot Mills (at Kings Dock Works, Swansea) when steam-engine driven. Note furnace on left of photograph and mills on right. The fly-wheels attached to steam engines dominate the Mill Bay.

General view of Hot Mills.

Hot Mill—furnaceman preparing to remove hot bars from furnace.

Furnaceman receiving 'doubled' sheet for re-charging into furnace.

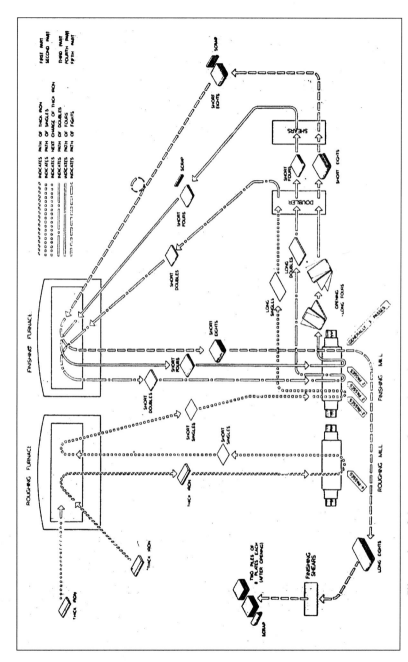

Illustration of the sequence of operations followed to produce blackplate on a Welsh Double Mill.

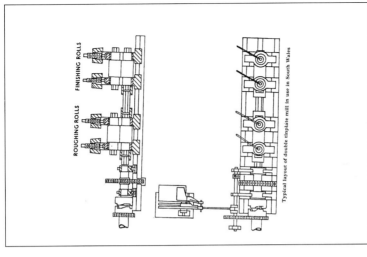

FINISHING ROLLS

ROUGHING ROLLS

Typical layout of double tinplate mill in use in South Wales

Typical layout of double tinplate mill in use in
South Wales.

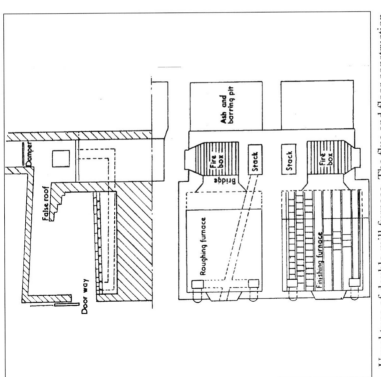

Damper

False roof

Door way

Fire box

Bridge

Stack

Stack

Fire box

Ash and
barring pit

Roughing furnace

Finishing furnace

Usual type of double-mill furnace. The flue and floor construction
varied according to personal opinion.

97

Rollerman feeding heated bar into Hot Mill.

On right of photograph the Rollerman is seen catching sheet as it is lifted over top roll by Behinder. The Doubler is on left of picture.

Doubler 'doubling' single sheet by bending with tongs and compressing with foot. Note protection against heat on clog on left foot.

Doubler completing sheet folding operation with 'squeezer' on crocodile shears.

Above and below, Hot rolling: opening of plates.

Overhead view of screw-down gear by which gap between top and bottom rolls in Hot Mill can be increased or reduced in size.

Initially, the pickling operation was performed by the Pickler and his assistants without any mechanical aids. The process, carried out in extremely uncongenial conditions, required individual sheets to be immersed and retained for a given period of time in a vat containing the pickling solution. The tongs used by the Pickler to place the sheets into the vat were also used to turn them in order to ensure overall surface contact with the solution. The use of a warm acidic solution was the subject of a patent presented in 1837 in which the containment of the solution in a lead bath partly immersed in a second bath of water heated by a furnace positioned underneath was also described.[21] This patent further mentioned the plates being placed on their edges in a rack or frame whilst within the vat.

Increasingly from about 1874 onwards the pickling operation became mechanised. The application of mechanical movement was not the invention of any particular individual but an evolutionary process involving contributions from many tinplate makers (e.g. Morewoods of Llanelli and Hopkins, Rees and Thomas of Aberdulais) and the manufacturers of tinplate equipment. Of the latter, the Millbrook Engineering Company of Landore, Swansea and H.F. Taylor, Struvé, Eaton and Price Ltd. of Neath made particularly noteworthy contributions.[22] The first machine used extensively within the trade was the three-arm central pillar type which, simplistically, consisted of three cradles which could be moved in a circular motion around a central pillar. The first cradle station catered for the loading/unloading of plates, the second enabled the cradles and the plates in them to be immersed into the pickling solution whilst the third allowed the cradle to be immersed into a washing tank in which clean, running water washed the acid solution off the plates. Having been manually pushed into position overhead each station, a piston valve arrangement facilitated the raising and lowering of the cradles into the tanks. When immersed in the solution the contents of the cradles were agitated by mechanical action to ensure an even de-scaling operation.

Under normal circumstances, the cycle of loading, pickling, washing and unloading lasted approximately one hour with the sheets remaining for about half that time in the solution of boiling sulphuric acid (heated by steam) at about 7% concentration. Eventually, the central pillar system was replaced by the continuous track arrangement patented in 1879 by David Grey but later modified and improved by others. This system consisted of an oval shaped overhead runway, a section of which passed over aligned acid and water tanks. Steam cylinders lifted the cradles into and out of the tanks but the movement of the cradles from one tank to another and the loading and unloading of the plates into the cradles was again performed manually and remained so until the demise of the hand mill plants.

The black pickling operation just described preceded the black annealing stage of the process during which the sheets were subjected to a heat 'soaking' to remove all moisture, soften the steel and release the stresses introduced into the sheet during rolling. Annealing involved the manual stacking of sheets to a height of three to four feet on a shallow cast iron bed-plate over which, when fully loaded, was placed a cast iron cover. The junction between the bed-plate and the cover was sealed with sand to ensure that uniform conditions existed within the pot whilst stationed in the annealing furnace. It would appear that before 1830 the annealing operation was carried out without a cover being placed over the sheets. The use of the cast iron covers reduced the risk of the sheets oxidising in the heat which would impair their metallurgical and surface qualities.

102

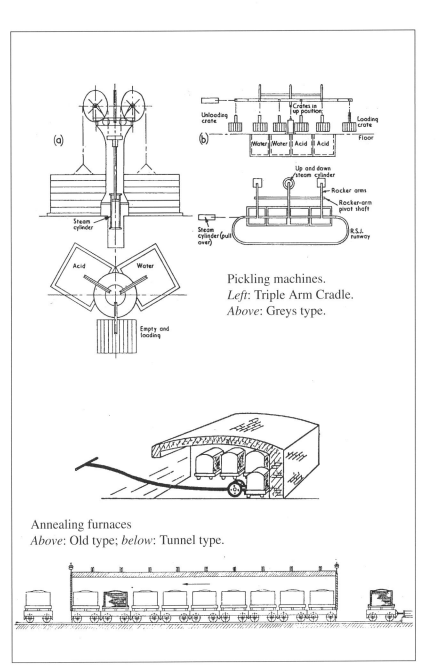

(a)

(b)

Unloading crate

Crates in up position

Loading crate

Floor

Water Water Acid Acid

Up and down steam cylinder

Rocker arms

Rocker-arm pivot shaft

R.S.J. runway

Steam cylinder (pull over)

Steam cylinder

Acid Water

Empty and loading

Pickling machines.
Left: Triple Arm Cradle.
Above: Greys type.

Annealing furnaces
Above: Old type; *below*: Tunnel type.

The labour-intensive method of annealing commonly employed before 1900 required the eight-man crew to manoeuvre, by means of a long-handled, two-wheeled trolley, a number of annealing pots into the furnace. When fully charged the reverberatory furnace was sealed off, fired by coal to the temperature required, maintained at that temperature for the specified period and then allowed to cool before being opened and unloaded of its charge. Later, an electrically driven charging device replaced the hand trolley. First patented by J. East in 1887 but not introduced until the early part of the twentieth century, the new design furnace took the form of a tunnel through which pot-carrying trolleys ran on rails.[23] As each trolley with its pot entered the furnace at one end, the line of trolleys within the furnace was pushed (or pulled as the case may be) one trolley-length forward discharging a trolley of fully-fired plates at the other end. The fire-grate (coal or oil fired), positioned at each side of the central section of the furnace, formed the hot zone. The motive power for the movement of the pots through the furnace was provided either by hydraulic ram or by a system of pulleys and wire ropes pulled from overhead by an electric crane.

The practice of introducing a non-oxidising atmosphere, such as coal-gas or nitrogen, into the pots during the cooling period produced a plate known as 'silver finish' because of its almost oxide-free nature. After the temperature had fallen to a level below that at which oxidisation occurred the covers were removed, exposing the annealed sheets to the atmosphere. The cooking stage of the annealing process usually lasted between ten and fourteen hours; a further forty-eight hours was required for cooling and unloading.

When annealed and cold, the sheets were individually passed through three sets of cold rolling mills—aligned in sequence and connected by conveyors—to both close the grain (thereby reducing the tin absorbency rate) opened up during annealing and impart a highly polished surface on the plate. Unlike hot rolling, the function of cold rolling was not to alter the dimensions of the sheet but to improve its quality and properties prior to the application of the tin coating. The roll housings for the cold mills were similar to, if lighter than, those for the hot mill. Each was fitted with two pressure screws for increasing or decreasing, by means of long-shafted spanners, the gap between the pairs of rolls within each mill. The feeding of the plates to the first set of cold rolls was undertaken by hand, a conveyor system thereafter transporting the plates from the first to the second and third pairs of rolls. Before the advent of conveyors the sheets had to be man-handled from one set of rolls to the next.

Pickling operation. Equipment is triple-arm cradle. Note central support column.

Pickling operation. Loading plates into cradle attached to triple-arm pickling machine.

Pickling operation. Unloading plates from cradles on Greys-type machine.

Workers in Pickling Department using Greys-type machine.

Pickling operation. Manually moving cradles on Greys-type machine.

Greys-type pickling machine.

General view of Annealing Bay. Furnace is on right of photograph.

The malleability introduced into the sheet at the black annealing stage to a large extent was removed during cold rolling. The reinstatement of this property was achieved by the second annealing— termed white annealing because by now the sheets had acquired a lighter coloured and more reflective surface, contrasting with the darker non-reflective surface of the sheets prior to cold rolling. The procedures followed in white annealing were much the same as those for black annealing. In fact, in some works the same furnace was used although the temperature was lower and the annealing time shorter for white annealing. After cooling, the sheets were subjected to a second pickling (white pickling) to release from the surface any traces of oxidation formed during cold rolling and annealing. In white pickling the acid strength (3% to 4% concentration) was lower than for black pickling. Following white pickling the sheets were ready for the application of the tin coating.

Annealing. Stacking plates on cast-iron base.

Annealing.
Stacked plates on base.

109

Charging Annealing Furnace—hand method (Teilo Works, Pontardulais).

Annealing. Manoeuvering covered stack of plates into furnace using trolley.

Annealing. Track-type furnace through which covered stacks of plates were
pushed or pulled on wheeled bogies.

The earliest method of tinning, that of manually dipping each sheet into a molten bath of tin as viewed by Diderot has been described earlier. Diderot's description of early eighteenth century tinning operations is unique for its detail as secrecy, it appears, was paramount amongst the tinners practising their craft. Although sparse on detail, the Reverend Richard Warner's account of what he saw at Ynysygerwn, near Neath, in 1798 in all probability represents the method of tinning employed in Wales when the industry began at Pontypool. 'The plates', he reported, 'are plunged vertically into a pot containing melted tin, the surface of which is covered with pitch, suet, or some fatty substance to prevent the calcination of the tin, and to make the surface of the iron more inclined to receive its coating. By this immersion the tin immediately unites itself to the plates and they are taken out completely tinned'.[24] Six years later, Donovan, another visitor to South Wales, tells of the 'single plates being dipped three times and the double plates six or more times'.[25]

If Warner's account can be taken as correct then certainly the process underwent significant changes over the next twenty years for we find in a report on his 1818 visit to Wales, Dr. Pococke, Bishop of County Meath, Ireland, mentioning a full battery of six pots,[26] an arrangement that remained in use until displaced by the Morewood tinning set sometime between 1866 and 1870. Dr. Pococke described how the plates were first placed into a pot containing hot grease, then into a pot of molten tin from where they were transferred into the wash-pot which had two compartments. In the first compartment of the wash-pot the plates were given a second coating of tin and upon removal were brushed on both sides with a hemp brush before being dipped in the second compartment from where they were offered to the grease pot, the temperature of which was set high enough to allow superfluous tin to run off. From the grease pot the plate was removed to the cooling pot. The plate now had a small bead or 'list' of solid tin along its lower edge. To remove this, the lower edge was placed in the 'list' pot—a shallow bath of molten tin. After a few moments immersion, the plate was taken out of the pot and struck sharply with a stick, causing the 'list' to fall away.

The consumption of tin in 1857, at 9 lbs per box for charcoal plates and 8 lbs per box for coke plates, was high by later standards. But even these levels represented a considerable improvement on the 13 lbs per box level of consumption reported in 1750. After the introduction of the Morewood pots in 1874, tin consumption fell to 4½ lbs per box.

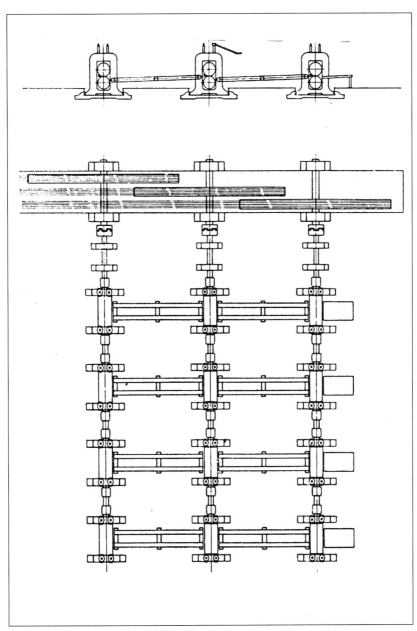

Layout of cold rolls.

General view of Cold Rolling Department.

Cold rolling. Feeding sheets through Cold Rolls.

Defects which might appear in plates which must be identified before tinning.

In 1703, four grades of tinplates were available viz. 'cross double', 'ordinary double', 'cross single', 'ordinary single'; the doubles measured 16½ by 12 inches, and the singles 13 by 10 inches. The weight of 450 'tinned plates' packed into a barrel was stated to be '2 cwt for ordinary singles and 3 cwt for the same number of ordinary doubles, similarly packed'.[27] Before the advent of mechanised tin pots, great reliance was placed on the judgement of the tinner to determine the correct thickness (weight) of the tin coating. Of course, what was an acceptable weight of coating to one tinner was looked upon with disdain by another. The consequences of this lack of uniformity was that common quality standards could not be established until mechanisation largely removed the element of operator discretion.

The installation of rolls in the tinpot to assist the tinman undertake the tinning operation was first proposed in a patent granted in 1843 to E. Morewood and G. Rodgers, originally metal merchants of Birmingham but later owners of the South Wales Tinplate Works at Llanelli.[28] Many patents, each presenting a variation on the basic theme, were filed following that of Morewood and Rodgers. The

115

tinning pots incorporating these adaptations or modifications were often recognised either by the names of the patentees or the location of the development work. For example, familiar names in the trade were the Player pot (after John Player of Clydach,), the Edwards pot (after Daniel Edwards of the Dyffryn Works, Morriston), the Taylor pot (made by the engineering firm of Taylor, Struvé, Eaton and Price Ltd. of Briton Ferry), the Cookley pot, the Abercarn pot, the Melingriffith (or Thomas and Davies) pot and the Poole-Davies pot.

In essence, the tinning operation following mechanisation was a relatively straightforward affair. Each tinning set or stack (there were normally several in a single tinning shop) consisted of two tinning pots containing the molten tin, a grease pot (all heated by furnaces positioned underneath) and a cleaning and polishing machine. In some cases the latter was not an integral part of the tinning set but a separate piece of equipment. The sequence of operations began with the sheet entering the pot through a layer of flux floating on top of the molten tin. The flux, initially palm oil but zinc chloride from about 1875 onwards, served a number of purposes: it prevented the molten tin from calcining upon contact with the air, it also cleaned the sheet, removed any moisture and generally prepared the surface for the adherence of the tin coating—a process that took place at a high temperature. Rolls and guide plates conveyed the sheet from the tinpot first into the washpot—also containing molten tin—the function of which was to remove any excess tin deposited on the sheets and from there into the greasepot to ensure an even consistency of tin coating. Following its extraction from the grease pot, any oil residue on the surface of the newly-tinned plate was removed by immersion in a hot soda solution prior to the cleaning and polishing operation.

During the period 1930 to 1960, the four types of hot-dip tinning machine principally in use within the trade were Players, Abercarn, Thomas and Davies (Melingriffith), and the Poole Davies (Aetna Standard). The last two were fully automatic, the feeding and pickling processes being part of the machine; however, a separate pickling plant was necessary in the Player and Abercarn machines. After white pickling and washing the plates were not allowed to dry and become stained but were kept in large vats of clean water. Removal of the plates from the vats and their submission to the entry end of the tinning machine was a manual operation but upon entering the machine they were mechanically conveyed through the fluxing, tinning, and cleaning sections by means of rollers and guides.

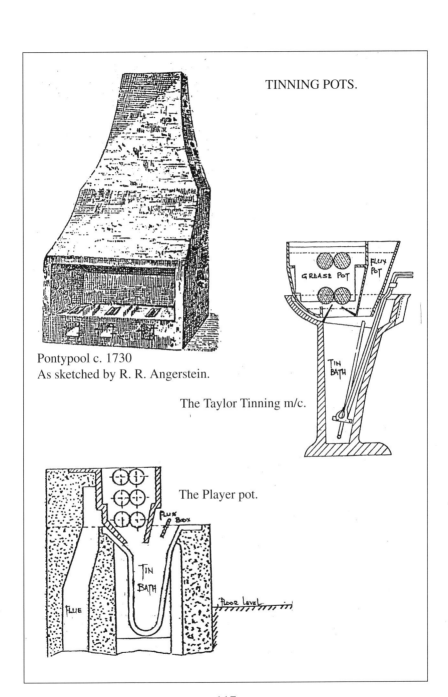

TINNING POTS.

Pontypool c. 1730
As sketched by R. R. Angerstein.

GREASE POT

FLUX POT

TIN BATH

The Taylor Tinning m/c.

FLUX BOX

TIN BATH

FLUE

FLOOR LEVEL

The Player pot.

117

With the Thomas and Davies (Melingriffith) machine the operations of feeding, pickling, swilling, tinning and cleaning were all combined and automatic. Whereas in the earlier machines no more than two plates could travel through simultaneously, the width of this machine allowed four plates placed sideways on, or even six if placed lengthways, to travel through together. The operation commenced with the loading of the blackplates onto the four (or six) receiving tables. From these they were lifted by means of rubber suckers positioned at the end of semi-rotative arms; sand, sprinkled between the individual plates whilst being stacked, preventing more than one sheet at a time being lifted. The suckers conveyed the sheets to and released them in a lead-lined pickling bath, containing sulphuric acid at about 10-15% concentration, steam heated to just below boiling point. When exiting from the acid tank, the sheets, now free of all oxide, were squeezed between rubber rollers to remove excess acid. The rollers also conveyed the plates through the washing section where water jets sprayed on both the top and bottom surfaces.

The tinning section consisted of two semi-circular cast-iron baths heated from below by means of coal, gas, oil, or electricity in which ingots of tin were reduced to a molten state. After swilling in water the plates were conveyed into the first bath of molten tin via a flux solution of zinc chloride which assisted the adherence of the tin to the surface of the plate and, by means of a system of rollers and guides, from there passed into the second or soaking bath. Here they proceeded through the molten tin to emerge vertically, assisted by three pairs of special hard-steel rolls running in a bath of molten palm oil. It was at this point in the tinning process that the amount of tin on the plate was controlled. The oil kept the tin on the sheets molten whilst the rolls, by capillary action, squeezed excess quantities of tin from both surfaces of the plate. Asbestos or soapstone brushes wiped the rolls clean of tin build-up and the tin removed flowed down through the oil to the tinpot below. The quantity of tin allowed to remain on each sheet (and thereby determining the quality) was controllable by the tinner adjusting the pressure of the brushes on the rolls.

Any residual palm oil remaining on the sheets after emerging from the pots was removed by cleaning machines. In these, an absorbent medium, e.g. hardwood sawdust, bran, or wheatings was used, to which was added a small amount of material such as calcium sulphate ('pink meal'). As this medium quickly soaked up the oil, constant replenishment was necessary.

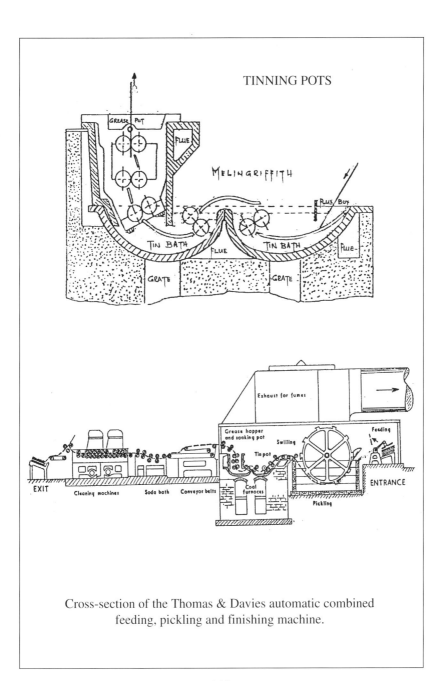

TINNING POTS

Cross-section of the Thomas & Davies automatic combined
feeding, pickling and finishing machine.

One of the earliest types of cleaning machine consisted of two semi-circular tanks each containing a layer of cleaning material. Plates conveyed through the first tank were coated with the cleaning material on one side and, as they emerged, were simultaneously turned over and coated on the reverse whilst in the second tank. On leaving the machine the plates passed through a series of polishing rollers covered with sheepskins, which dusted and polished their surfaces. In another machine, designed on the 'S' principle, the plates were conveyed by rollers through two curved dishes, one positioned above the other, in which the cleaning medium rested.

However, it was the Aetna type of cleaning machine, as attached to the Thomas and Davies pot, that gained widespread favour within the trade. At some works the sheets were conveyed through a hot solution of soda and soap to remove all traces of oil before being offered, whilst still wet, to the Aetna machine. The machine was of horizontal construction, the plates being conveyed through it by a series of rollers, which also agitated the cleaning material, keeping it in motion. Chain cup elevators gathered the material from the tank bottom, and delivered it via screw conveyors to the top of the machine. Several pairs of rolls, built up by compressing several swansdown buffing discs into a laminated form, were driven by endless chains on the outside of the machine. Each pair of rolls rotated at different speeds, the top roll in one pair travelling faster than the bottom, while in the next pair the bottom roll turned more quickly than the top thus subjecting both sides of the plate to a series of brushing operations. As the plate left the machine most of the cleaning medium was brushed off by static brushes through which the plate passed before finally being buffed and polished by several high-speed sheepskin covered disc rollers.

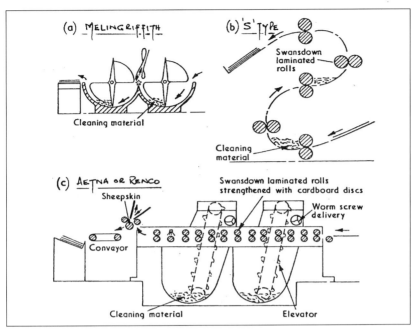

Types of cleaning machine.

General view of Tinhouse (Old Castle Works, Llanelli).

121

Tinhouse at King's Dock Works, Swansea.

View of Player Dipping and Morewood Re-rolling Tinpot
installed at Clayton Works, Pontardulais.

Single Sweep Tinpot made by Harrop and Benson Ltd and installed at
Clayton Works, Pontardulais.

Entry of plate into Tinpot.

The finished tinplates were automatically stacked for transportation to the inspection or assorting tables. Here they were carefully examined for defects and sorted into grades, viz. primes, seconds, wasters, waste-waste, light and heavy gauge sheets, and menders. The final operations were reckoning i.e. counting into the required number of sheets, followed by weighing and packing ready for shipment. For many years all tinplates were packed in birch, elm, or other hardwood boxes (the term 'basis box' originated from the early method of packing) in quantities of about 2 cwt. per box. With the development of improved road transportation and loading and unloading facilities the application of wooden stillages (platforms) and cardboard and paper packaging reinforced by metal corner pieces and strapping enabled the weight of tinplate within a single 'bulk' (or pile) to be increased to around one ton.

Rather than achieve the exact size of plate required by a customer at the hot rolling stage, for reasons of economy manufacturers sometimes rolled and tinned sheets to twice or even three times the ordered size. For example, sheets of dimensions 28 by 20 inches perhaps would be produced for an order calling for sheets of 14 by 20 inches. The larger

Thomas & Davies Patent Combined Automatic Feeding, Pickling, Tinning & Finishing Machine installed at Melingriffith Works, Cardiff.

'Dusting' of plates after Tinning.

sheets would be cut to size (i.e. two sheets of 14 inches by 20 inches) on a rotary shearing machine, usually hand fed though later designs incorporated an automatic feed arrangement. The plates requiring shearing were submitted to the nip of the cutting discs via a pair of revolving shafts that conveyed the plates through the machine.

The total manufacturing time in the old style hand mills plants ranged between 140 and 170 hours depending on conditions encountered during the production sequence, the type of equipment installed and the layout of the works. The average processing time for each stage of manufacture was as follows:[29]

	Hours
Hot Rolling	24
Black Pickling	1 to 2
Black Annealing and Cooling	74
Cold Rolling	1
White Annealing and Cooling	58
White Pickling	1 to 2
Tinning, Assorting, Packing	3 to 4
	162 to 165

Assorting and Reckoning of Tinned Plates.

126

Tinplate boxed and ready for shipment at Old Castle Works, Llanelli.
(Note brand name: Castell.)

Ashburnham Works, Burry Port, near Llanelli.

Burry Works, Llanelli.

Aber Tinplate Works, Llansamlet, Swansea.

128

Ystalyfera Tinplate Works, c. 1890.
Each of the fourteen stacks on the right-hand side of the building was positioned above a tinning pot. From the photograph we know that, at the time it was taken, the Ystalyfera Works had fourteen tinning sets.

Lydney Tinplate Works, West Gloucestershire.

129

The buildings of the hand mill era were easily discernible on the South Wales skyline by the series of short stacks that rose above the tinning sets and through which the fumes generated by the tinning process were emitted to the atmosphere. Housing the various production departments together with boiler houses, fitting shops, carpenters shops, stores for the raw materials (tin, fluxes, greases, acids, wood etc.), warehouses and offices, to the eye they were either inoffensive mid-nineteenth century masonry work, utilising native stone and/or local brick, or an untidy sprawl of makeshift structures, principally steel framing covered with corrugated sheeting, or, as was more often than not, a combination of both styles of construction. Whilst most of the old style works have now been demolished and their sites cleared some, either fully or in part, remain standing having been adapted for other purposes. Of those remaining, the Treforest Tinplate Works situated two miles south of Pontypridd on the west bank of the River Taff is of particular interest, not only because it typifies the style of construction but also because the tinplate manufacturing techniques employed at the Works was captured by T.H. Thomas (1839 to 1915) in a fine collection of twelve water colours now deposited in the National Museum of Wales, Cardiff.

Of greater interest, perhaps, is the Kidwelly Works near Llanelli where thanks to an enterprising group of local enthusiasts both buildings and machinery have been restored as the centre piece of an industrial museum. Similarly, the National Trust, having acquired the site of noted industrial archaeological importance to South Wales at Aberdulais, Neath, has excavated and re-constructed the sixteenth century copper smelter and what remains of the iron forge and tinplate works that operated on the site in the eighteenth and nineteenth centuries. A visit to both sites is recommended.

The cost of constructing a tinplate works and installing the necessary plant and equipment obviously varied with size and the date of construction. In 1831, the Conway Works at Pontrhydyrun (near Cwmbrân), consisting of a single mill, was valued at £3,354; in 1854 the cost of constructing the two mills and tinhouse at the Morfa Works (Llanelli) amounted to £7195. In 1866 the cost of erecting a new works of three mills at Pontardulais was estimated at £20,000 but in 1873 the Morlais Tinplate Works at Llangennech was erected for just £16,000. The Elba Works at Crymlin Burrows, Swansea, the last old-style works to be built, cost the joint owners, Baldwins Limited and the Anglo-Asiatic Petroleum Company, the comparatively substantial amount of £200,000 to build and equip in 1925.[30]

Old-style tinplate works were not ostentatious affairs; they were perhaps little more than manifestations of William Blake's 'dark satanic mills'. A few displayed limited aesthetic qualities when viewed externally. The Dyffryn Works, Morriston, for example, must have caught the eye when first built not because of any architectural fluency but because of the functional relationship between purpose, design and form of construction—features which could be expected when the founder of the works was not only an experienced tinplate maker but also a highly respected stonemason. This works (now demolished), formerly situated to the south of the A40 at a point adjacent to the west bank of River Tawe and just below the Wychtree Bridge at Morriston, is important historically not only because of the noteworthy contributions of Daniel Edwards to the development of the tinplate industry, but also because of the evidence of its past which has survived the passage of time.

The Lower Swansea Valley, i.e. the area consisting of the flood plain of the River Tawe extending south westwards from Clydach to Swansea Bay, has had an association with the metal working trades since the early part of the eighteenth century. Commencing with the smelting of copper, metals worked in the locality included gold, silver, lead, iron, steel, nickel, zinc and cobalt and one of the earliest tinplate manufacturing enterprises in Wales was established at Ynyspenllwch, near Clydach, in the first half of the eighteenth century. Tinplate production in the newly-created industrial town of Morriston (Morris's Town after its founder Sir John Morris) began with the conversion of an old corn mill situated upon the Upper Forest Farm into the Upper Forest forge, later developed into the large Upper Forest and Worcester Steel and Tinplate Works whose employees numbered in excess of two thousand.

Daniel Edwards—stonemason, entrepreneur, inventor, philanthropist —was the prime mover for the creation of the Dyffryn Steel & Tinplate Works which, when in full production, provided employment for almost 2,000 citizens of Morriston. Having been engaged in his trade as a stonemason on extensions to the Ystalyfera Tinplate Works and the Upper Forest Tinplate Works and the construction of the Worcester Tinplate Works, the basic knowledge of tinplate engineering practices he must have thus gained was supplemented by periods of employment at the Landore Tinplate Works and the Beaufort Tinplate Works where, presumably, he acquired experience in the techniques of tinplate production.

131

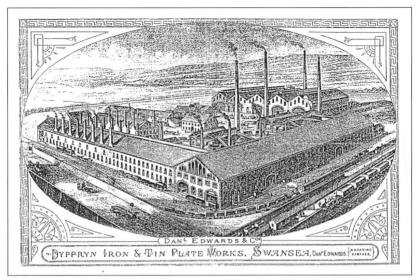

Dyffryn Works, 1895. Note the original position of the tin house on extreme left of print (building with two sets of low stacks running parallel with road).

Dyffryn Tinplate Works, Morriston (1953).

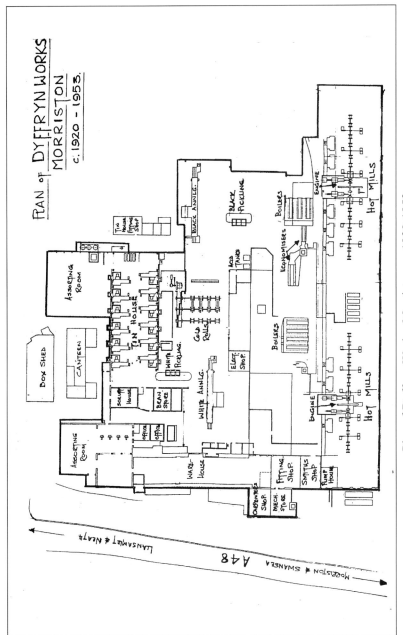

Plan of Dyffryn Works, Morriston, c. 1920-1953.

Just what stimulated Edwards to embark on the creation of the Dyffryn Works is not known. Furthermore, there is no indication of how the venture was financed except that, at first, he may have been involved in a form of partnership.

For details of the historical development of the Dyffryn Works (or, for that matter, any other British tinplate works) E.H. Brooke's *Chronology of the Tinplate Works of Great Britain* and its subsequent *Appendix* are invaluable and, in the main, authoritative sources of information. It is from this publication that we have an indication of the earliest existence of the Dyffryn Works for reference is made to a Neath Abbey Ironworks drawing of stands and mill bed plates for D. Edwards of Morriston dated 1871. Brooke also reports that a three-mill tinplate works driven by steam power was erected in 1874 by Messrs. Daniel Edwards and J. Davies, trading as Daniel Edwards & Co.

Subsequent expansion of the initial development meant that by 1895 the Works consisted of eight tinplate mills, employing approximately four hundred male and female workers. Ownership of the works at this time passed into the hands of Daniel Edwards's son, W.H. Edwards, with the original company, 'Daniel Edwards and Co.', being wound up. Conceivably coinciding this event, work commenced on the erection of plant and equipment to produce steel by the open-hearth method on a site adjacent to the tinplate works. A report published in 1895 gave the following description of the Works:

The length of the building occupied by the mills and cold rolls is 309 feet, height from floor 22 feet. It is admirably lighted by two rows of windows, placed close to each other. The span is 60 feet, and the roof is one of extraordinary strength. The scouring and annealing house is 180 feet long, the tin house and warehouse is 212 feet long, and this brings the total length of the building up to 701 feet. In other words, to pass through the establishment from one end to the other means a walk of a little more than an eighth of a mile.

The Works stand on property of about 10 acres—tinplate section 6 acres, steelplant 4 acres—and are equipped with eight mills and eleven pairs of cold rolls. Power is supplied by two fine engines and five boilers of the Galloway type. The two flywheels of the engines are each 22 feet in diameter and 38 tons in weight. The plant also includes one 10 ton steam hammer and two of 5 tons, the former of which is among the finest in the country. For the production of steel bars for working into tin and terne plates, the firm has at the present time in operation two of Siemens's open hearth furnaces, and two more furnaces are in course of construction to meet the requirements of a rapidly growing trade. There are also large regenerators for purifying the gas from the furnaces, and a chemical laboratory for the careful testing of all metals and materials used in the industry.[31]

The third decade of the twentieth century saw the ownership of the Works change hands on two occasions. In January 1920 Sir John Bryn Edwards (grandson of Daniel), having previously inherited the works from his father, W.H. Edwards, sold it to a consortium comprising Messrs. Llewellyn Davies, Frank R. Phillips, David Richards, R. Tilden Smith, and Leon Vermont for £793,919. The new company, trading under the name of Dyffryn Works Ltd., was registered in February 1920 with a capital of £1,000,000. However, this venture was relatively short-lived as trading ceased in September 1923 following the acquisition of the Works in the previous month by the Grovesend Steel & Tinplate Co. Ltd. By this time, the plant configuration consisted of fifteen tinplate mills and five Siemens' open hearth steelmaking furnaces.

Subsequently, no further expansion took place and according to Brooke the next event of significance was the sterilisation in 1946 of four of the fifteen tinplate mills under the Tinplate Redundancy Scheme leaving eleven mills operating. In May 1947, as part of a major re-organisation of the South Wales steel and tinplate industries, the tinplate side of the business was acquired by The Steel Company of Wales Limited, the steelworks remaining in the ownership of Richard Thomas & Baldwins Limited, Richard Thomas & Co. having acquired the entire works in the earlier takeover of the Grovesend Steel & Tinplate Co. Ltd.

And so began decline of the Works that lead eventually to its closure. When in full production its contribution in terms of output to the total amount of steel and tinplate manufactured within the South Wales was not insignificant. In 1949 for example, the Works was capable of producing approximately 15,000 basis boxes of tinplate per week from eleven mills and 2,000 tons of steel per week from the five open hearth furnaces.

In January 1953, tinplate production ceased and the Works buildings were used merely as a storage area for tinplate produced at the Velindre Works. The Works had a minor reprieve in October 1954 when the manufacture of terne plate (the coating of steel with an alloy of lead, tin and antimony) was introduced following the closure of the Byass Works at Port Talbot. It was reported that the steel base for the manufacture of the terne plate was obtained from the Pontardawe Steelworks: it must therefore be assumed that by then steel manufacture at Dyffryn was in the process of being run down prior to its termination in 1956. The furnaces themselves were later dismantled and the buildings housing them and associated structures demolished.[32]

The need for suitable packaging materials for the tinplate manufactured at Trostre, Velindre and Ebbw Vale resulted in the 1955 conversion of the Works by The Steel Company of Wales Limited to manufacture these products. This activity continued at Dyffryn until December 1981, when the British Steel Corporation, the then owners, decided to cease all operations at the Works, its final closure taking effect in the early part of 1983.[33]

The importance of Dyffryn Works in terms of the tinplate industry's technological advancement reflects the ingenuity and foresight of Daniel Edwards. It was Edwards whom Sir William Siemens, James Riley (Siemens's Works Manager at Landore) and others chose as a collaborator in the experiments to apply steel, manufactured by the Siemens Open Hearth method at the nearby Landore Steel Works, to tinplate production.[34] Steel produced by the Bessemer process had earlier been tried for tinplate manufacture at the Dafen Works, Llanelli, but these trials had proved unsuccessful. The improved quality of the steel produced by the Siemens Open Hearth method in combination with the expertise of Daniel Edwards and his employees at the Dyffryn Works were key factors in the first successful application of steel to tinplate manufacture.

Further testimonies to Edwards's ingenuity are the 'Edwards Patent Tinning Machine' and the use of zinc chloride as a flux in the tinning operation to replace the more expensive and less effective palm oil. The Edwards Tinning Machine was designed to eliminate the need for the Washman in the tinpot crew and by doing so reduced the cost of the tinning operation from 7 old pence (3p) to 4 old pence (1½p) per box.[35] The machine (or the concept employed) was subsequently adopted by many other South Wales tinplate manufacturers, the consequential productivity benefits and cost savings placing the South Wales industry in a stronger position to compete with overseas tinplate producers.

The use of zinc chloride as a flux, although cost and quality effective, at first proved to be a source of irritation amongst tinhouse workers who viewed with concern the fume emission from the new flux. The flux was subjected to exhaustive tests by medical practitioners and noted chemists and the conclusions drawn were that its use was less injurious to health than the palm oil it replaced. The results of the tests so satisfied the tinhouse workers that a subsequent opinion survey taken amongst those of them who had gained practical experience of both types of flux found the majority to be in favour of zinc chloride.

The Dyffryn Works occupied 6.01 acres of ground leased from the Duke of Beaufort, the principal landowner in the locality. Water for process purposes was extracted from the nearby river and from the Swansea Canal which passed within a quarter of a mile of the Works and which also afforded a convenient means of transportating coal, tin and finished tinplate to and from the Works. Even more convenient were both the adjacent main road leading to the port of Swansea and the Swansea Valley line of the Midland Railway to which the works was connected by a short-length spur.

An 1895 illustration of the Works shows the tinning shop in a position parallel to the main road although the plant layout at the Works was altered during the last thirty years of its life as a place of tinplate manufacture. For the industrial archaeologist, the following description of the buildings and plant installed may be of interest:

Original Tin-house (later converted to an Assorting Room)—a single storey rectangular building constructed of solid uncoursed random stonework set in mortar. The working area originally consisted of sixteen tinning bays, eight on each side, recessed into the main structure of the building under arched flues over which were constructed the short stacks for the emission of fumes. The arches were bricked up after the construction of the new tin-house erected in the 1920/1930 period.

Both the north and south walls were interspersed at regular intervals on two levels by windows which in character and design were typical of the late nineteenth century. The Bower windows at ground floor level offered light and possibly ventilation.

137

The building was some 100 feet in length by 66 feet wide and the roof, originally of slate but later sheeted, was supported by fifteen wooden trusses.

Hot Mill Building—Of dimensions 540 feet long by 60 feet wide the building was constructed of random stonework in mortar and interspersed with window openings at regular intervals on two levels on the west side with the east side covered with corrugated sheeting. The roof trusses were supported by cast iron columns.

Pickling Bay—Approximately 270 feet by 7 feet in dimensions the walls being part brick/part steel framed and sheeted construction. Steel roof trusses supported by steel stanchions and covered with corrugated sheets.

Cold Rolls and Annealing—Part brick/part steel frame and sheets walls, steel stanchions supporting light steel trussed and sheeted roof. Approximate dimensions 385 feet by 60 feet.

The small assorting room (85 feet square) and outbuildings such as the box shed (for making packaging boxes), the blacksmiths', carpenters' and fitting shops, the stores, garage and canteen were all of typical late nineteenth century random stone/brickwork set in mortar constructed with slated roofs. The covered floor area within the Works approximated to 120,000 square feet.[36]

The physical characteristics of the Dyffryn Tinplate Works when in operation in 1952 were as follows:[37]

Number of Employees	Male	482
	Female	135
	TOTAL	617

Bars accepted at Works:

Quality	Basic or acid steel
Approximate	Length 14 to 16 feet
Average Weight per foot	19 lbs

138

Hot Mill Furnaces:

Number of Furnaces	14
Capacity	10 Boxes per hour
Composition of Charge	32 to 36 pieces
Heating Period	45 to 60 minutes each heat
Temperature Control	Hand controlled air pressure
Lining	14 inches refractory brick
Fuel	Oil
Cleaning	Undertaken at week-ends.

Hot Mills:

Number of Mills	11 Pairs of Welsh Mills
Capacity	Approximately 11,000 boxes per week
Mill Drive	Steam direct

Mills Rolls:

Length	26, 28 and 30 inches
Diameter	22 and 24 inches
Chill	¾ inch maximum
Frequency of Regrinding	Weekly
Composition	Cast Iron
Analysis	Carbon 2.8% to 3.4%
	Silicon 0.75% to 0.8%
	Sulphur 0.08% to 0.12%
	Phosphorous 0.3% to 0.4%
	Manganese 0.3% to 0.35%
	Molybdenum 0.25%
Lubrication	Hot neck grease—hand applied
Life	Variable but 96 days maximum
Weight	Varied between 1 ton 15 cwts to 2 tons 18 cwts.

Plate sizes from Mills:

Maximum Width	28 inches
Maximum Length	33 inches
Sizes Possible to Roll	Maximum 30 inches x 25 inches Minimum 20 inches x 14 inches
Average Substance	98.76

Pickling:

Type of Vat	Taylor
Dimensions	7'6" length x 5'9" breadth x 4'4" depth

Acid Strength	Black 7%
	White 3%
Temperature	Black 95°C
	White 85°C
Acid Change	Black—twice per day
	White—weekly

Annealing furnaces:

Number	2
Type	Tunnel
Fuel	Coal
Temperature Control	Damper
Length	77 feet
Capacity	12000 basis boxes
Lining	18 inches refractory brick
Temperature	Black—800°C to 850°C
	White—650°C

Cold Rolls:

Number of Trains	4
Drive	Steam driven rope pulley
Size	Smallest—36 inches by 21 inches
	Largest—42 inches by 24 inches

Tinpots:

Number	13
Type	Melingriffith
Fuel	Oil
Capacity	15,000 basis boxes per week (approx.)
% Waste/Waste of Make	1.59

A peculiarity of the tinplate trade was the brand names given to different categories of tinplates produced by individual companies; in the case of the Dyffryn Works the brand names were 'D.E.' 'IWEN' and 'ONEN' for charcoal plates and 'DANBERT', 'ACORN', 'DERI' for coke plates. By means of the brand names, normally burnt into or stamped onto the packing cases, it was possible to identify the place of manufacture. Other examples of brand names are: [38]

Old Castle Works, Llanelli	Coke Plates	'CASTELL and 'OLD CASTLE'
	Best Coke	'OC'
	Charcoal	'STRADEY'
	Best Charcoal	'BURRY'
	Extra Charcoal	'KILLEY'
	Super Stamping	'CASTELLITE'
Teilo Works, Pontardulais	Coke plates	'SARDIS' and 'IROS'
	Best Coke	'TEILO'
	Charcoal	'DEVA' and 'KHARTOUM'
	Best Charcoal	'ERIE'
Grovesend Works, Gorseinon	Coke plates	'ETON' and 'BRENIN'
	Best Coke	'H.F.'
	Charcoal	'W.L.A.'
	Best Charcoal	'DANUBE'
Ffrwdwyllt, Port Talbot	Coke Plates	'E.D.S.'
	Charcoal	'PENRHYN'
	Best Charcoal	'FROOD'
Melingriffith, Cardiff	Coke Plates	'ELYN' and 'PEN'
	Charcoal	'TYNANT' and 'R.G.'
Abercarn, Gwent	Coke	'AC' and 'AC BEST'
	Charcoal	'ARRAN', 'ABERCARN' and 'GWYDDON'
Lydney, Glos.	Charcoal	'DEAN', 'LB', 'LYDNEY' 'ALLAWAYS BEST', 'R. T. & CO'. and 'KYRL'

NOTES

[1] Reaumur, R-A.F. de, *Principles de l'art de faire le fer-blan* (Histoire de l'Academie Royale des Sciences, Paris, 1725).

[2] Powle, H., *Philosophical Transactions* (1676).

[3] Jeans, J.S., *The Iron Trade of Great Britain* (Methuen, London, 1906).

[4] 'Poolpe' (a non-de-plume), *Historical Survey of the West Wales Steel Industry* (an essay submitted at the Royal National Eisteddfod of Wales at Llanelli in 1930).

[5] Diderot, M. (Pub.), *Encyclopedie ou Dictionnaire Raisonne Des Sciences, Des Arts et des Metiers par une Societe de Gens de Lettres* (Paris, 1756) .

[6] Ess, T.J., op. cit., also Gale, W.K.T., *Iron and Steel* (Ironbridge Gorge Museum Trust, 1979).

[7] Ess, T.J. op. cit.

[8] Ibid.

[9] Ibid.

[10] Plot, R., *The Natural History of Staffordshire* (1686).

[11] Llwyd, E., *Philosophical Transactions* (1697).

[12] Angerstein, R.R., *Resa Genom England* (Mss in the Riksarkivet, Stockholm and referred to in Rhys Jenkins Collection, National Science Museum).

[13] Davies, H.L., *The Development of the Tinplate Trade* (an address given to the Iron and Steel Institute, 30.4.52).

[14] *Journal of the South East Wales Industrial Archaeology Society,* Vol. 1 (Nov. 1965).

[15] Minchinton, W., op. cit.

[16] Rhys Jenkins Collection, National Science Museum.

[17] Ince, L., 'Neath Abbey Iron Company', *Der Archasologische Pers.,* 1984.

[18] Minchinton, W., op. cit.

[19] Hayes, G., *A Guide to Stationary Steam Engines* (Moorland Publishing, 1981).

[20] Jenkins, Rhys, 'The Early Days of the Tinplate Industry' (*Transactions of the Neath Antiquarian Society,* 1930-31).

[21] Ibid.

[22] Ibid.

[23] Ibid.

[24] Warner, R., *Second Walk Through Wales—August and September 1798* (Bath, 1799).

[25] Donovan, E., *Descriptive Excursions through South Wales and Monmouthshire in 1804* (London, 1805).

[26] Cartwright, J.C. (Ed), *The Travels through England of Dr. Richard Pococke Vol. II.*

[27] Quoted in Jenkins, Rhys, op. cit.

[28] Ibid.

[29] Davies, H.L. op. cit.

[30] Brooke, E.H., op. cit.

[31] *Ports of the Bristol Channel*, 1895.

[32] British Steel plc., Archives: *The Steel Company of Wales Ltd.*

[33] Ibid.

[34] *The Cambrian*, 24th July 1906.

[35] *Industrial World*, 11th October 1895.

[36] Papers in Author's Collection.

[37] Ibid.

[38] Brooke, E.H., op. cit.

5. CONFLICT AND CONCILIATION:
AN EXAMINATION OF THE EMPLOYER/EMPLOYEE
RELATIONSHIPS WITHIN THE INDUSTRY

'And I also think that too many employers still do not understand that from now on, socialism or no socialism, they must work with their employees.

A genuine spirit of co-operation means more than the most elaborate paternal welfare schemes. It is the employer who still acts as if he belonged to another and far superior order of humanity who is heading for trouble.

J.B. Priestley.

(Reporting in the *Daily Herald* of 13th October 1947 after having visited tinplate and steel works in Llanelli).

By today's standards, the conditions under which tinplate workers in the old-style hand mill plants performed their tasks were unrelentingly onerous. It is the often drawn conclusion that employees who have little or no influence over the factors that bring about their odious working environment become antipathetic towards their employers. Reactionary, militant attitudes are usually expected of an exploited workforce; attitudes that sometime manifest themselves in the tough, uncompromising postures adopted by representatives of the workforce in their dealings with their employers, especially over matters that appear to be singularly beneficial to the latter.

More often than not and contrary to all expectations, the tinplate workers of South Wales displayed unusually high degrees of moderation, discipline and progressiveness in their dealings with their masters. Inevitably within a pluralistic industrial society such as that of South Wales over the past two centuries conflicts of interests arise that cannot be settled quickly and amicably. These may escalate to the stage where one side or the other seeks a resolution through forceful means. In the case of the tinplate industry the occasions when either masters or men resorted to precipitant action in support of their aims were minimised because of the mutual desire to defuse potentially explosive issues by discussion and joint analysis of the problems faced. This was particularly evident following the establishment in 1899 of a formally constituted organisation through which representatives of the employers and the employed were able to consult on matters of common interest, negotiate changes in the terms and conditions of employment and refer disputes through an agreed procedure.

Undoubtedly, it was the enlightened attitude of the employees and their representatives that played a major part in the adoption of these measures. Not only did they display a sense of moderation when pursuing claims for improved conditions but also they took great interest in events and factors impinging on the future course of the industry. In reciprocal manner, amongst the works owners were a few who sought to improve wherever feasible the conditions of employment within their establishments through the recognition of and dialogue with workers' representatives. As many of the tinplate works owners and managers were born and bred in South Wales they may have understood, if not always accepted, the aspirations of their employees.

But tinplate manufacturers were not always of local stock. During the nineteenth century entry into the trade had come from a variety of sources, including some from outside of Wales. Merchant firms from Liverpool (the location of the tin smelting industry and a major port for the export of tinplates) and Birmingham (the centre of the domestic market for tinplate) in particular invested extensively in tinplate manufacturing enterprises. In 1838, for example, the Ystalyfera Works (which within ten years of its founding was said to be the largest tinplate works in the world) was built by the Liverpool based firm of Treacher and James whilst it was J.S. Tregonning, a tin and metal merchant also of Liverpool but with additional interests in Cornwall, who founded the company that erected the Morfa Works, Llanelli in 1851. The over-riding reason for the merchants' involvement in the manufacturing side of the business was the assurance of a supply of tinplate for their merchandising activities during periods when demand for the product out-stripped total manufacturing capability—one of the factors that forced the non-manufacturing merchants to pay higher prices. Of the Birmingham based merchants who injected capital into tinplate manufacture, E. Broughton & Co. of the Hendy Works, Pontardulais and Messrs. E. Morewood and Rogers, who owned the Cwmbwrla Works, Swansea and the South Wales Works at Llanelli were to play significant roles in the subsequent development of the industry.[1]

At the primary end of the business, iron makers also sometimes extended their interests into tinplate manufacture in order to ensure a regular outlet for the product of their furnaces and forges. Richard Fothergill, a partner in the Tredegar Ironworks, acquired the Caerleon Works in 1818 whilst J.T. Smith and Ernest Trubshaw (who later became the first Chairman of the Welsh Tinplate Industry's Joint Consultative Council) iron-founders of Barrow-in-Furness, both held shares in Llanelli's Western Works. Similarly, companies supplying tinplate works with equipment and other materials used in the process sought to protect the markets for their products by investing in tinplate manufacturing firms. Typical of this group was John Player of Clydach who involved himself in tinplate manufacture after having been engaged in the foundry trade supplying equipment to tinplate works. The Gibbins family of Neath, the Bevan's of Briton Ferry and the Lewis's of Gorseinon all entered the trade after having achieved some success as manufacturers and suppliers of the sulphuric acid used in the pickling stage of the process.[2]

Until the development of the large conglomerate during the period between the two World Wars, the owners of or principal shareholders in tinplate manufacturing enterprises more often than not took an active interest in the running of their businesses, assisted by managers and foremen experienced in aspects of the technical operation. Among those who held managerial positions were individuals who themselves later became owners or shareholders after having laboured in the trade from early youth, moving from job to job in the internal hierarchy and learning the secrets of the manufacturing processes as they progressed through the ranks to their senior positions. Often, these were striking personalities toughened by their hard struggles and made wise by having experienced the bad times with the good. Fiercely independent they may have been but their individualism did not preclude their appreciation of the benefits derivable from co-operation with their fellow manufacturers on matters of common interest.

Reference has already been made to Daniel Edwards of the Dyffryn Works, Morriston and it would be wholly unjust not to include in any historical analysis of the tinplate industry a comment on the career of Richard Thomas (1838 to 1916) whose name, perhaps more than anyone else's, is synonymous with the South Wales steel and tinplate trades.

The son of a London metal merchant, Thomas began his career in the tinplate industry at the Margam Works, Port Talbot. After acquiring a basic knowledge of the trade at Margam he left in 1863 to

Richard Thomas.

take up the position of cashier and under-manager supervising the construction of the Melyn (Neath) Works under the direction of the owner, Mr. P.W. Flower. Realising that the demand for tinplate was soon to exceed supply, a few years later he borrowed funds and together with others formed a company which acquired the Ynyspenllwch Works at Clydach where, as Managing Director, he controlled all aspects of the business. In 1871, a dispute with his co-directors caused him to leave Ynyspenllwch and take a lease on the Lydbrook Works in Gloucestershire, then comprising two mills and a forge, under the title of his own firm viz. Richard Thomas and Company.

In 1875 he bought the nearby Lydney Works consisting of four mills; two years later, in seeking to secure a supply of coal for his Works, he acquired the Lydbrook Colliery—an event that quickly led to the bankruptcy of the Company because of the excessive costs incurred in keeping the pit dry. Nonetheless, undeterred by this setback, he re-formed the Company to operate, exclusively, the Lydney and Lydbrook Works. This new arrangement obviously met with success for in 1884 Richard Thomas and Company was

Forge of Melyn Tin Works, 1878.

Tinning House at Melyn Tin Works, 1878.

147

registered as a limited liability company with a capital of £50,000. In 1888 the Company acquired the Melingriffith Works, Cardiff which under the astute guidance of Richard Thomas was re-organised and expanded to accommodate ten mills by 1893, making it one of the largest works in the trade. After his death in September 1916 at the age of 78, the Company's development continued, initially under the authority of his immediate descendants but later through the business acumen of professional managers, to a position of dominance over the trade. By a series of shrewd acquisitions the Company eventually controlled over forty percent of the available tinplate manufacturing capacity within the United Kingdom.[3]

The Company's status was duly acknowledged by a visit of HRH The Prince of Wales to the Cwmfelin Works in Swansea on the 19th June 1919. A plaque, appropriately printed on tinplate, produced and distributed to the work force in commemoration of the visit listed the Company's activities as tinplate production from twelve tinplate works with, in total, one hundred and fourteen mills; steelmaking from two steelworks with a total of seventeen open hearth furnaces; an engineering works and foundry; a brickworks together with three associated companies with interests in coal mining and shipping. Annual outputs were stated to be 250,000 tons of steel ingots, bars and billets, 4,500,000 boxes of tinplate and 250,000 tons of coal produced by a total of 10,000 employees. In 1945, the Company's influence on South Wales became even stronger because of the amalgamation of its interests with those of Baldwins Limited, a company involved mainly with steelmaking but which also was actively engaged in coal mining and, to a lesser degree, tinplate manufacture. The new Company, known as Richard Thomas & Baldwins Limited (R.T. & B.), had under its control roughly two-thirds of the productive capacity within the trade.[4]

In general, the owners of steel and tinplate works in South Wales were not imbued with an overwhelming desire to acquire immense wealth or unassailable power; there was not to be found amongst them the like of Andrew Carnegie, for example. Seemingly content to obtain no greater a return on their investments than that which ensured a comfortable existence and a measure of security for them and their families, the majority of tinplate works owners lived within the local communities—admittedly in palpably more agreeable circumstances than those who served them—enjoying a status befitting their

148

positions. Several families, notably the Tregonnings of Llanelli, the Myers and Gibbins of Neath and the Gilbertsons of Pontardawe, remained in control of tinplate companies for several generations and were instrumental in the economic and social development of their adopted districts.[5] Some sought to enhance their parochial power by successfully contesting national or local government elections, their positions in the community ensuring the support of a large section of the local population even if, when elected, they perhaps neglected the interests of the electorate, preferring instead to protect those of their own class.

Domestic comfort for these privileged members of South Wales society often meant a large house of distinctive style incorporating the latest sanitary features and services and containing several bedrooms and reception rooms and a large dining room. Servants' quarters and stables for the horses and carriages also featured widely in these commodious villas. Usually sited within easy travelling distances of the works to which they owed their existence they were agreeably positioned, more often than not within a substantial parcel of land and having a long drive curving its way to the front entrance through well laid out gardens. In the absence of the local land-owning aristocracy and gentry (i.e. the Duke of Beaufort and the Earl of Jersey), steel and tinplate works owners aspired to emulate their peers in their social habits. Dinner parties were a regular feature amongst the members of the South Wales upper-middle class society and it was likely that the cost of a single dinner party given by a tinplate works owner exceeded the annual income of the majority of his employees. Attendances at concerts and the theatre in Swansea were also favoured pastimes. Nannies and governesses were engaged to look after the children until the boys, especially, were old enough to be despatched to an appropriate Public School and University or the Armed Services as a prelude to the 'young master' eventually returning to the fold to oversee the activities of the business.

The maintenance of the conventions of Christian thought and deed was important to the tinplate masters, manifestly displayed in their support for the construction and upkeep of places of worship within the tinplate districts. William Gilbertson not only worshipped at but also financially supported churches at Cwmavon and Pontardawe; his son Arthur, again a deeply religious man (he was organist and choirmaster at St. Peter's Church, Pontardawe), in 1886 donated the

Arthur Gilbertson.

£3000 required to construct All Saints Church in the town in memory of his father.[6] But perhaps the greatest single testimony to the tinplate makers Christian awareness was that of Daniel Edwards of the Dyffryn Works in Morriston. Edwards generously assisted, both in financial terms and as a skilled stonemason with advice on the style and method of construction, the efforts of the people of Morriston to build their 'Tabernacl'—the so-called 'Cathedral of Welsh Non-Confirmity' because of its size (it is the largest chapel in Wales) and imposing aspect—in the town in 1873.[7]

Generally, the owners of tinplate works in South Wales displayed the qualities highly esteemed by Victorian society. As hard working moralists they imposed a stern discipline on the work-force and demanded acknowledgement of their status; woe betide a worker who did not display the customary respect when in the presence of his or her employer. Discourtesy often meant dismissal—an action which usually precluded the employee from further employment in the trade in South Wales. Offended employers unhesitatingly passed on information about the dismissed worker's misdemeanour to fellow employers.

Glanrhyd House, Pontardawe, home of the Gilbertson family. This photograph was taken during the period of World War I when the house was used as a temporary hospital.

Conforming to the Victorian ethos, the more wealthy amongst the employers paradoxically sought salvation by tending to the spiritual needs of their less fortunate brethren whilst caring little for their physical well-being. However, a few of the more enlightened individuals, perhaps conscious of their social responsibilities, also endeavoured to improve the secular aspects of life within the tinplate communities, portraying paternalistic attitudes towards their employees and their families. This was particularly true of the various owners throughout its lifetime of the Melingriffith Works at Whitchurch, Cardiff, where a scheme for basic medical care for the workers was introduced as early as 1775. The educational needs of employees at the Works, too, were acknowledged by the owners assembling a library and providing a reading room for their use. A school for their children was established before the end of the eighteenth century.

The first Melingriffith school was the fore-runner for others in the trade. Promoted by the Harfords (of Quaker stock) who, from about 1785, owned the Works in conjunction with the Partridge's, the school, according to the Work's accounts, was in operation around 1786-7. It would seem, however, that this early attempt at educating tinplate workers and their offspring did not exist for very long. If it did, it was probably incorporated within a fresh venture launched in 1808 and again based on the Melingriffith Works but with subscriptions also derived from public sources. Despite the external assistance, the greatest proportion of the school's income came by means of deductions from the earnings of the Melingriffith workforce for it was noted in the initial subscription list that six sawyers had contributed 6 shillings (30p); seven scalers 15 shillings (75p) and seven tinmen 21 shillings (£1.05p.). During 1809, a total of 62 children were reported as having attended the school, drawn from the districts of Whitchurch, Eglwysilian and Pentyrch.[8]

The second tinplate works school was probably that associated with the Margam Tinplate Works at Taibach, Port Talbot. The school, founded in 1829 whilst the works was in the ownership of Robert Smith (formerly of the Carmarthen Tinworks), at that time was one of four educational establishments within the parish of Margam.[9] A Government sponsored enquiry into the employment of children in factories conducted in 1833 reported the school as having a population of 50 males and 40 females, with the cost of running the enterprise supported partly by the Margam Tinworks Company and partly by contributions from the workforce. Individual workmen paid 9d. (4p.) per month towards the upkeep of the school, initially held in a single room attached to the tinworks but later boys and girls were segregated into two schools with populations of 65 and 106 respectively. An indication of the conditions within the schools is given in the report of a Government Commissioner who visited them in 1847:

I visited this school on the 4th March. In the boys' school at twenty minutes past nine, only 14 children were present. The schoolroom lies above the stables of the works. It is in the shape of gnomon; ill-furnished, and ill-calculated for a schoolroom. The master appeared unintelligent and untrained. I visited the girls' school whilst a muster was being made of the boys. On my return I heard 13 read . . . the girls' school contained no furniture but benches. I heard six girls read (viii) St. Matthew, all very ill, they could answer hardly any questions.[10]

Ernest Trubshaw, owner of the Ashburnham (Llanelli) Works and first chairman of the Tinplate Trade's Joint Conciliation Board.

John Player, founder of the Player's Tinplate Works, Clydach, Swansea.

In 1825, William Llewellyn of Aberavon acquired the iron forge at Aberdulais and on the site built a tinworks and subsequently a school for the education of his workers' children. By 1842 the school had 42 pupils and individual workers were contributing 2d (1p) per week towards its upkeep. Two years later, the Carmarthen Tinworks had a school maintained partly by the proprietors (Wayne & Dunn) and partly by a levy on the workers of 1d. (½p) per week. Pontardawe (1846) and Ystalyfera (1850), both situated in the Swansea Valley, also had schools promoted by tinplate works owners, the former by William Parsons and James Palmer Budd in the case of the latter.

In the Llanelli district, the owners of the Dafen Tinplate Works, Messrs. Thomas and James Motley of Felinfoel and John Winkworth, a surgeon-dentist of Bath, in 1859 donated the £500 needed for the erection of a school adjacent to the works. The company also contributed £20 per annum towards its maintenance, supplementing the workers levy of 2½d (1p) in the £ per week. In 1886 the school had an average attendance of 168 and received the highest praise in the Inspector of Schools Report. Also at Llanelli, the re-building in 1873 of the New Dock School was assisted by a £100 contribution from two local tinplate manufacturers, J.S. Tregonning and E. Morewood.

Other tinplate works schools were at Hendy, near Pontardulais (1885), Ynyspenllwch (Glais), near Clydach in the Swansea Valley which opened around 1860, Melyn, Neath (circa 1872), Tydu near Rogerstone in Gwent (circa 1860) and the Amman Works School at Brynamman. The latter school, which began functioning in 1872, is of particular interest for two reasons; firstly, for the comment made by an Inspector in his 1873 report that: 'Lateness almost universal—conveying food to fathers at works' and secondly for the subsequent achievement of its first master, a young man by the name of Henry Jones. Appointed as teacher immediately after having left Bangor Normal College, he remained at the school for two years, leaving to take up other appointments that culminated in him holding the Chair in Moral Philosophy at the University of Glasgow. He later received a knighthood for his academic and public services.[11]

The paternalism of the owners, particularly those in West Wales, was evident in other spheres. Reports in *The Cambrian* newspaper portray how Messrs Hallam and Madge, the owners of the Upper Forest Tinplate Works in Morriston, took 700 of their employees on a day's outing Carmarthen in the summer of 1856, the owners and their families also participating in the excursion. So pleased were they with the good conduct of their employees that a promise was given that 'the outing would not be the last of its kind' but whether or not the commitment was honoured cannot be ascertained. What is known from other press reports is that some works proprietor's invited their employees to partake annually in what in one case was said to be 'a substantial supper'.[12]

Other masters, perhaps mindful of how they themselves had achieved their status, were keen to assist workers in other directions. John Jones Jenkins, for example, recognised the need for tinplate workers to have the opportunity of learning to read and, after having acquired the ability, to have access to books at a time when most tinplate towns did not possess a public library.

Sir John Jones Jenkins.

In John Jones Jenkins we have a fine example of 'worker-to-owner' progression in the tinplate trade. He not only became an astute and successful businessman but also a man with a strong sense of civic duty, displaying the typically Victorian values of sobriety, thrift, hard work, peity and respectability.

He was born in Clydach in the Swansea Valley but subsequently spent most of his childhood and early youth in Morriston, first entering the trade in 1850 when 14 years of age undertaking the most menial of tasks such as the bundling of offcuts or greasing the necks of the rolls normally required of boys. Obviously displaying a talent above his lowly status he quickly rose through the ranks to become a manager at the Upper Forest Works at Morriston when only twenty-three years of age. Whilst in that capacity he was instrumental in the acquisition of books for a library at the Works and the introduction of reading and music classes for the workers.

After having established himself as a leading figure in the tinplate trade by becoming a major shareholder in the companies that operated the Beaufort (Morriston) Cwmfelin (Swansea) and Yspitty (Loughor)

155

Works he took an active interest in civil and political affairs and was elected to serve as a member of the Swansea Borough Council in 1885, his diligence in civic matters gaining for him the Office of Mayor of the Borough in 1889. At his own expense he distributed 14,500 Testaments to the working class children of Swansea during his period of Office and strongly advocated the establishment of a public library in the town. He became the principal protagonist for the extension of the Mumbles Railway from its one-time terminus at Oystermouth through to its ultimate terminus at Mumbles and the construction of the Mumbles Pier as a recreational facility for the people of Swansea and surrounding districts.

In recognition of his public services, including two periods as a Member of Parliament for Carmarthen (1882 and 1895 to 1900), he was knighted by Queen Victoria at Windsor Castle in 1885 and elevated to the peerage in 1906, assuming the title of Lord Glantawe. Despite his business successes and the honours bestowed upon him he resided for a large part of his life in Bath Villa, the house he had built in Morriston, situated but a few hundred yards from Tabernacl Chapel in the centre of the town.[13]

In similar vein, members of the Lewis family of Gorseinon generously provided and supported social and welfare facilities for the inhabitants of the area and were instrumental in the establishment of a community hospital.

However, these isolated examples of philanthropy on the part of the owners did little to relieve the continuously burdensome tasks required of tinplate workers undertaken in what were normally draughty, poorly lit and ventilated establishments, often having little more than primitives sanitary facilities. In the smaller works where the manufacturing operations were carried out in a confined area the heat from the furnaces, in combination with the steam and fumes emitted by the pickling vats and tinning sets, created a particularly onerous working environment. This was made much worse in inclement weather conditions when low cloud settled like a cloak over the works, holding the fumes close to the ground. Under these conditions men, women and children laboured and strove to keep pace with the incessant rhythm of the mills and the sequence of operations in the pickling, the tinning and the assorting and reckoning sections. With earnings entirely related to output there was no respite or scope for complacency. To tinplate workers before benefits such as guaranteed earnings for lay-off periods or unemployment pay were introduced, the equation of no output equalling no pay equalling no food was not merely a theoretical assumption but a harsh reality.

The working conditions prevailing in tinplate manufacture before World War I inevitably had a detrimental effect on the physical well-being of the workforce. Apart from a few investigations into specific complaints from the work-people (for example the 1891 inquiry by Drs. Attfield and Morgan into the use of zinc chloride as a flux on the health of tinhouse workers) little information exists to enlighten contemporary researchers on the environmental aspects of work within eighteenth and nineteenth century tinplate works. However, early in this century two detailed surveys were undertaken, the results of which depict a fairly bleak picture of the physical consequences of employment in tinplate manufacture. Fostered by the trade union movement and the growing awareness of the need to monitor and record the conditions of employment within Britain's factories, the first survey—carried out in 1901 at the request of British Steel Smelters, Mill, Iron, Tinplate and Kindred Trades Association which represented tinplate millmen—established that the average age at death of a tinplate worker was no more than thirty-two years. Eleven years later, a comprehensive examination of working conditions in the tinplate trade was undertaken by two Government appointed Factory Inspectors viz. Dr. Collis and Mr. Hilditch. One aspect of their study compared the average ages at death of workers in different employment classifications, including tinplate manufacture. The following table, portraying information extracted from their Report published in 1912, indicates that the average age at death of a tinplate workers at 45 years (46 years for tinhouse workers, 43 years for millmen and 47 years for others) compared unfavourably with that for a coal miner at 51 years, a carpenter at 59 years and the longest living of all, a gardener at 68 years. However, these figures, although indicative of a relatively low life expectancy, cannot be interpreted as an accurate representation of the overall position as they were based on but a small sample (i.e. circa 1.5%) of those employed in the trade.[14]

AVERAGE AGE AT DEATH OF TINPLATE WORKERS COMPARED
WITH OTHERS IN DIFFERENT EMPLOYMENT CLASSIFICATIONS

Source: Collis, E.L. and Hilditch, J., *Report on the Conditions of Employment in the Manufacture of Tinplate*, Comd 6394 [1912])

OCCUPATION	AVERAGE AGE AT DEATH (YEARS)	TOTAL NO. OF DEATHS USED TO DETERMINE AVERAGE AGE AT DEATH
Farmers Grazier	67	101
Gardener, Nurseryman	68	50
Shoemaker	64	132
Blacksmith	57	278
Carpenter, Joiner	59	332
Tailor	62	103
Cutler, Scissors Maker	53	1139
Bricklayer, Mason	53	333
File Maker	53	275
Coal Miner	51	142
Furnaceman	49	87
Tinplate Maker	45	360

The premature ageing and short life expectancy of tinplate workers identified by these surveys is understandable if viewed against the background of the age at which most employees started work in the trade, especially in the period before legislation made it illegal for children to be employed in factories until in their early teens. In the log-book of the Hafod (Swansea) Copperworks School is an entry against the date of 10th June 1863 which states: 'A boy named Fudge left school today to work in the Tinworks, Landore. Age: 9 years'.[15] By the time he and many of his contemporaries had reached, if they were lucky, fifty years of age they would have served a sentence of '40 years hard labour'! The 1911 investigation of Collis and Hilditch revealed a higher incidence of respiratory diseases, especially phthisis (pulmonary tuberculosis), amongst tinplate workers than for other sections of the population. Rheumatism and associated diseases also seemed to be more prevalent within the group, especially amongst the mill crewmen exposed to the heat of the furnaces and metal whilst performing their physically demanding tasks. The report went on to suggest that employees of the old style tinplate plants were also more likely (i.e. by comparison with national averages) to develop cancer and diseases of the nervous and urinary systems.

Commenting on their results, Collis and Hilditch remarked: 'these data show the age at death of this class of operative to be exceptionally low and the age constitution unfavourable'. Their observation on the unfavourable age distribution of employees within the trade was upheld by an analysis, based on the 1911 Census, of the ages of almost 23,000 tinplate employees. This identified a distinct bias towards young workers as the following table illustrates.

AGE DISTRIBUTION OF TINPLATE EMPLOYEES IN 1911

(Sources: Collis, E.L. and Hilditch J., *Report on the Conditions of Employment in the Manufacture of Tinplate*, Cond 6394 1912 Census of Population 1911)

AGE GROUP (YEARS)	NUMBER IN GROUP			% IN GROUP	CUMULATIVE &
	M	F	TOTAL		
10 to 14	830	121	951	4.14	4.14
15 to 19	4297	1401	5898	24.79	28.93
20 to 24	3299	744	4043	17.59	46.52
25 to 34	4289	308	4597	20.00	66.52
35 to 44	3595	148	3743	16.29	82.81
45 to 54	2520	59	2579	11.22	94.03
55 to 64	1027	19	1046	4.55	98.58
65 to 74	296	2	298	1.30	99.88
75 and Over	27	—	27	0.12	100.0
	20180	2801	22982	100.00	

Evidently from the above table, almost half the work-force was aged under twenty-five years and only 17.19% of the group exceeded forty-four years of age at a time when compulsory retirement and occupational pensions schemes were non-existent. The conclusion to be drawn from this analysis is that by the age of fifty the majority of tinplate workers had either left the industry to seek less arduous employment or, as is more likely, had laboured themselves to a premature grave. No words better describe the physical consequences of employment in tinplate manufacture than those uttered on 17th July 1936 by Ernest Bevin, then General Secretary of the Transport and General Workers Union. In an address on the subject of the introduction of a pension scheme for tinplate workers given to a meeting of the industry's Joint Industry Council, he succinctly, yet revealingly, stated:

> What we have done has lengthened life—happily, I think. I know I am in a district where you sing and praise the virtues of the palaces beyond the skies; but we like to stay here as long as we possibly can. Yes, happily with our health services and with all our other efforts we have prolonged the average duration of life by eleven years. In the old days we did not have to argue so much about a Pension Scheme; the cemetery solved it.[16]

Women and children, too, suffered physically from their employment in the tinplate trade. Cuts especially, sometimes deep incisions, and grazes caused by handling the sharp cornered sheets were frequent occurrences. The 1833 Report of the Commissioners on the Employment of Children in Factories noted that young females employed in the Margam tinplate works were prone to chlorosis (green sickness), a disease associated with a blood deficiency.

Hard, demanding work in uncongenial conditions faced those seeking employment in tinplate manufacture. But with few alternative means of earning a living available in South Wales the industry magnetically attracted workers. Employment opportunities peaked in 1928 when just over 32,000 were engaged in the trade (see Appendix B for table of employment statistics). The numbers employed in individual establishments varied with the equipment installed and the demand for the product but indicative levels are approximately 850 operatives for an eighteen mill plant and 290 for a six mill plant, grouped occupationally as in the following table.

160

INDICATIVE MANNING LEVELS AND OCCUPATIONAL GROUPINGS FOR TINPLATE WORKS CONSISTING OF EIGHTEEN MILLS AND SIX MILLS

(Source: Trade Returns in Author's Collection)

	NUMBER OF OPERATIVES FOR A PLANT OF								
	18 MILLS					6 MILLS			
	ADULTS		YOUNG PERSONS		TOTAL	ADULTS		YOUNG PERSONS		TOTAL
	M	F	M	F		M	F	M	F	
Bar Cutting	11	—	—	—	11	4	—	—	—	4
Furnacework and Doubling	108	—	—	—	108	36	—	—	—	36
Rolling and Behinding	108	—	—	—	108	32	—	4	—	36
Shearing and Bundling	18	—	29	—	47	6	—	8	—	14
Opening	—	35	—	9	44	—	14	—	4	18
Pickling (black and white)	6	15	—	19	40	4	5	—	4	13
Annealing (black and white)	40	—	—	—	40	11	—	—	—	11
Cold Rolling	4	—	82	7	93	4	6	10	15	35
Tinning and Rinsing	100	—	34	—	134	39	—	7	—	46
Cleaning and Dusting	—	8	—	5	13	3	—	—	7	10
Assorting and Reckoning	18	6	—	—	24	6	3	—	—	9
Boxing	13	—	—	—	13	—	—	—	—	5
Mechanics, Enginemen, Labourers	140	—	10	—	150	35	—	8	—	43
Other Spare Hands	18	2	6	2	28	6	1	2	1	10
TOTALS	584	66	161	42	853	191	29	39	31	290

NOTE: Young persons were employees aged seventeen years and under.

In addition to the above, a manager, a few foremen and office workers were usually employed. They numbered, in total, no more than twelve for an eighteen mill plant and six for a six mill plant.

161

Group of boys employed in a tinplate works, *c.* 1910.

The mill crew consisted of four grades viz. the Rollerman, the senior man in the crew responsible for setting the mill to ensure that the sheets produced were of the required gauge (thickness) and length, the Doubler who folded the sheets, the Furnaceman and finally the Behinder who, as the name suggests, stood behind the mill and caught the sheet with a pair of tongs as it emerged from between the rolls and with an extremely dextrous movement passed it back to the Rollerman over the top of the upper roll. Output per crew during an eight hours stint varied between two and three tons (40 to 60 boxes) of plates depending on the size ordered and rotative speed of the rolls within the mill—normally around forty revolutions per minute, but varying depending on the power source used. The manhandling of up to three tons of steel continuously for eight hours under ideal working conditions is itself a feat of endurance. However, because of the repeated sequence of rolling and heating, each ton of plates rolled had to be handled five times in temperatures averaging 24°C and in an atmosphere laden with the fumes given off by the burning of lubrication grease placed on the hot necks of the rolls inter-mixed with the coal and ash dust emitted from the furnaces. Under these

162

circumstances, by today's standards, the physical feats of the mill teams can only be described as Herculean. Although ducted fresh air systems introduced in later years went some way towards ameliorating the stifling atmosphere of the mill area little could be done to lessen the physical exertion required of the millmen themselves until continuous strip mill technology was introduced into the trade from the late 1930's onwards.

The typical uniform of a mill crewman in the old hand mill plants consisted of the 'crys bach' (small shirt)—an open necked, short sleeved shirt of Welsh flannel, the ideal material for the absorption of perspiration—trousers, canvas apron and neck and head scarves (again to absorb perspiration). Clogs were worn on the feet and strips of canvas or leather were tied around the shins and ankles to give protection from the hot bars or sheets as they were passed along the mill floor from the Furnaceman to the Rollerman. The cost of this clothing, so essential for their personal safety, had to be met in full by the workers as the employers neither provided any free-of-charge nor gave their employees allowances towards the cost.

Furnaceman charging furnace, c. 1900.

Hot Rolling. Rollerman feeding plate to Hot Mill, *c.* 1900.

As previously stated, the operation of separating each sheet from the 'pack' formed during rolling invariably was performed by female 'Openers'. Two or three women or girls on a day shift dealt with the output, i.e. 6 to 9 tons, produced by a single mill over a twenty-four hour period. Usually working 8.5 hours per day on weekdays and 6 hours on Saturdays (48½ hours per week), each Opener, some barely sixteen years of age, lifted and carried packs of between 60 and 70 pounds in weight and processed between 5,000 and 7,000 sheets during a normal working day, weighing between 2¼ and 3 tons.

The pickling processes, black and white, provided work for both male and female employees. During the early part of this century when the 'roundabout' type pickling machine was in common use the pickling department of a six mill plant required for its operation a total four men viz. two Picklers and two Wheelers, supported by nine to ten female employees, the number depending on circumstances, to operate it.

Hot Rolling. Female openers 'opening' (i.e. separating) plates after hot rolling, *c.* 1900.

As with 'Opening' the output of a single mill achieved over twenty-four hours was easily matched by the pickling department operating on a day shift system, comprising 5 weekdays of 8.5 to 9 hours per day plus 6 hours on a Saturday. Within the working week an average of 80 tons of steel (179,200 sheets) were physically lifted by the pickling crew into and out of the pickling machine cradles. Girls of sixteen and seventeen years of age were to be observed carrying weights of up to 62 lbs., each load of plates having to be raised from a low ground position and carried across wet floors to the cradles positioned some twenty feet away in what was a back-breaking task.

Dense clouds of acid vapour permeated the atmosphere within the pickling department causing irritation to any abrasions or lesions of the skin, especially those around the nostrils and mouth. The acid-saturated atmosphere caused the teeth of pickling employees to blacken and it also advanced the decaying process. Women employed in the pickling department usually wore heavy clogs on their feet and covered their legs with thick woollen stockings to minimise the risk of cuts from the sheets. Thick serviceable aprons, consisting of either two layers of sacking covered with a layer of tarpaulin or a single layer of sacking covered by a thin sheet of iron or steel with the edges turned in to prevent lacerations to the hands and arms protected the trunk from being doused with acid or water during the loading/ unloading procedures. For the same reason, male Picklers and Wheelers bound their legs with strips of sacking or tarpaulin and wore tarpaulin aprons. The girls covered the upper part of their clogs with 'tow rags', i.e. strips of tarpaulin, to prevent an ingress of water. Acid spillages quickly destroyed clothing and footwear and, as with the mill crew, replacement was at the employee's, not the employer's, expense.

Group of mainly female tinplate workers 'openers'
(Baglan Bay Works, near Port Talbot), *c.* 1920.

Annealing. Hand charging of Annealing Furnace, *c.* 1900.

Compared with other departments, work in the annealing section, or 'nail house' as it was commonly known within the trade, was less arduous. The Annealers, usually numbering eleven in a six mill plant, were not continuously exposed to high temperatures in the manner endured by the millmen. Furthermore, the physical effort required of them did not continue unabated throughout the shift as it did with millmen. More often than not, opportunities existed for brief respites between the periods when the furnaces required loading and unloading. However, burns to the hands and arms were frequent occurrences amongst annealing operatives.

The greatest proportion of young employees, i.e. those under seventeen years of age, was to be found in the cold rolling department. Here, young boys and girls worked nine hours each weekday and six hours on a Saturday (51 hours each week) feeding sheets through the rolls. In contravention of the Factories Acts, young people were sometimes employed on a two shift system made up of day and night stints of twelve hours each, Monday to Friday. In this department the

Cold Rolling. Boys feeding plates into Cold Rolls, *c.* 1900.

incidence of crushed fingers was high caused by inadequate guarding and the need for the youngster to hold onto a sheet for as long as possible before releasing to ensure a correct feed to the rolls. Severe crushing of the hand was often the result of the child having to wipe off any excess oil or grease from the sheet either with a rag or with his (or her as the case may be for girls were also employed on cold rolling) cap as it was presented to the rolls. If the child was not careful the cap became caught in the nip of the rolls pulling the hand with it. The lifting of heavy loads (up to 56 lbs. at a time) by young persons was also a regular feature of work in the cold rolling section and a frequent cause of injuries.

Tinhouse workers ran a considerable risk of accidents. Scalds from the molten tin and the hot flux and grease, crushed limbs from contact with revolving machinery such as shafts, rollers, pullups, gears and belting and severe lacerations from the sheets were commonplace. Employers were reminded frequently of the need to ensure that machinery guarding was provided and adequately maintained but until the post-World War II period these reminders mostly went unheeded. With ventilation totally inadequate for the conditions, the atmosphere within the tinhouse became particularly obnoxious. Fumes emitted by the flux pot and from burning palm oil combined with the dust particles arising from the material used for cleaning the plates created a working environment which increased the health risks to tinhouse workers. The two men, the Tinmen and the Riser, to each pot worked in temperatures ranging between 36°F and 39°F on a continuous three shift pattern, each shift consisting of eight hours, whilst other tinhouse workers, such as the female dusters and carriers, worked eight to twelve hours weekday shifts and a further six hour stint on a Saturday.

The environmental conditions of tinhouses and the effect on their health of the materials used in the process, particularly the palm oil flux, were a constant source of concern for tinhouse employees. Early investigatory work undertaken in 1891, 1899 and 1901 was largely inconclusive on the question of the long-term effects on the health of tin house workers of the uncongenial working conditions. Only as a result of vigorous campaigning by Collis and Hilditch following their 1911 study were ventilation systems within tinhouses improved, reducing both the discomforts endured by the workers and the risks to their health.

Except for the customary half-hour meal-break, production operatives within the tinplate trade established a rhythm of work that was maintained throughout the shift—physically exertive work undertaken in stifling conditions created by high temperatures and humidity. Coal and ash dust in the mills, the irritating fumes of the pickling section and the tinhouses, the 'sharps' (sweepings of flour mills) used in the cleaning and dusting stages of the process all permeated through the air. The loss of body fluid under these conditions was exceptionally high. To have viewed the appearance of the millmen in particular would have brought a tinge of realism to the observation 'wringing with perspiration' for it accurately described a familiar sight in the hand mills when, at the end of each shift, the highly absorbent Welsh flannel 'crys bach' was removed and the perspiration wrung from it.

Enhanced by the dust and fume laden atmosphere, the need to quench the thirst and replenish the body with fluid was paramount if the energy sapping dehydration process imposed on the millmen was to be countered. Evidently, the consumption of beer on their premises was a practice condoned by many a works owner, anxious to obtain a

Tinning. Tinman and Riser working tinpot, c. 1900.

Tinning. Dusting machine, c. 1900.

profitable level of performance from his employees and knowledge-able about the deleterious effects of dehydration. 'Old-timers' still talk of individual workers who regularly consumed at least fifteen pints of beer during the course of a shift and immediately after. The number of public houses surviving today that were situated within a few minutes walking distance of a tinplate works give these reports a measure of authenticity. Young boys were despatched with the empty 'sten' (i.e. a tinplate or enamel pitcher capable of holding approximately one pint) to the nearby public houses charged with the responsibility of returning posthaste without having spilt a drop of the thirst quenching liquid for the men. Women workers in the tinplate trade, too, we known to occasionally imbibe the amber nectar. Workers who displayed greater wisdom or who were totally abstinent consumed instead either ginger beer, oatmeal tea or cocoa in order to avoid the attacks of stomach cramp or colic that sometimes developed after the quaffing of cold beer.

Not only were the women workers oftentimes the equal of their male counterparts in the consumption of alcohol but also in the use of factory floor expressions; no sweet terms of endearment but harsh and uncompromising language, echoing perhaps the prevailing circumstances. Charles Wilkins compiled his *History of the Iron, Steel and Tinplate Trades of South Wales* during the latter part of the nineteenth century and in a rather reflective mood wrote in the following manner of what he had seen whilst visiting a tinplate works at Morriston:

Now we come to the action of the girls and at the Morriston Works; it was remarkable with what dexterity they laboured. Slender girls some of them; some, too, of the old fashioned school, who appeared to have slipped from young girlhood into womanhood without any of that interesting epoch when a little of life's romances is enjoyed. Rather sad, thoughtful faces, to whom the whirl of the rolls was the monotonous over-ruling sound of life, and who had learned the table of troubles and sorrows without any blending of sunshine.[17]

Whilst Wilkins saw some of them as 'slender girls' there were others whose physique aptly fitted the description 'Celtic Amazons' and whose unfemininely calloused hands would be used to good effect on any pretentious individual. The nature and character of the work undertaken by women employed in the Welsh tinplate industry was certainly unique within the metal working trades, if not any industry.

They were subjected to prolonged and intense physical exertion in what were extremely uncongenial conditions. It is not surprising, therefore, to find the number of women employed in tinplate manufacture declining after peaking at just over 4300 (14% of all employees) in 1923, when employment opportunities in other industries, offering much less demanding work, began to appear in South Wales.

Traditionally, the extent to which employment opportunities existed within the tinplate trade varied yearly, even weekly under extreme circumstances. Recession, induced either by economic conditions (e.g. the 1837 to 1843 financial crisis in America that forced prices down from 47 shillings £2.30p per box to 25 shillings £1.25p per box), or political factors (e.g. the McKinley Tariff) produced long-term effects.[18] In the short term, it was drought, shortages of essential materials or major breakdowns of key plant and equipment that brought about interruptions to production and unemployment for the workers. Notwithstanding these impediments, the labour force gradually increased from a few dozen in the early part of the eighteenth century to well over thirty thousand by the second decade of the twentieth century.

With most of the tinplate establishments in the early days requiring only a small number of employees, the labour requirement for a works was met largely by recruitment from within the local community. However, no works could operate successfully without the applied skill and knowledge of experienced managers, foremen, rollermen and tinmen and where these could not be obtained locally they were brought from other districts of South Wales. Men who had proven their ability in one works were keenly sought after to fill vacancies in others and the 'poaching' of experienced employees away from their current employer was an accepted, if sometimes resented, practice. For example, in 1866 the Manager of the Morfa Works, Llanelli was approached about, but subsequently refused, offers of employment from the owners of both the Ynyspenllwch (Clydach) Works and the Treforest Works. Other experienced managers volunteered their services to prospective employers. When John Player of Clydach was considering re-opening the Gower Works at Penclawdd he received an application for the post of mill manager from a man already employed in that position in another works. In his letter of application the candidate temptingly suggested that: 'if you will be so kind to employ me I can bring a first-class staff of workmen along with me'—an indication that he was also prepared to act as the agent for the recruitment of workers.[19]

The inducement of housing at reasonable rents was used occasionally by employers to entice skilled workers away from rival firms into their establishments. In 1902, the Foxhole Tinplate Company, operating the Aber Tinplate Works at Llansamlet, charged their key workers four shillings (20p) per week for a three-bedroomed cottage and two shillings and sixpence (12½p) per week for or a two-bedroomed cottage owned by the company and conveniently situated adjacent to the works.[20] These were comparatively low rental values for the time.

Before 1870 when the union movement began to gain ground within the tinplate trade, a worker's terms and conditions of employment were determined by direct negotiation between himself and the employer or the employer's agent. The impression might be gained that agents were hard, unscrupulous men who seized any opportunity to gain an advantage for the master over his work-people. Although there may have a few agents displaying such tendencies, in general they were responsible and respected men who had served the industry over a long period and knew of the need to foster a reasonable working relationship with the work-force. Their employers would not have been pleased with the loss of key workers as a consequence of a vexatious relationship with the agent. A report in 'The Cambrian' newspaper (18th May 1866) commented on a presentation to Mr. Rees Griffiths, Head Agent at the Ynyspenllwch Works, to mark his forty years of service to the establishment as both employee and agent. The presentation ceremony was attended by the works owners and representatives of the workers and local chapels. The cashier to the Ynyspenllwch Tinplate Company presented Mr. Griffiths with a purse of money and gave the following address:

Dear and Respected Sir,
    The desire to give 'Honour to whom honour is due' has always beaten energetically in the heart of the Cymru. Their motto is the grandest among the nations—'Y Gwir yn Erbyn y Byd'. The workmen, and others employed at the Ynyspenllwch Tin Works duly appreciating your estimable character beg your acceptance of this purse of money. This they do as a mark of their admiration, their esteem, and their gratitude for your meritorious labours extending over 40 years in connection with these important works.

In looking back upon your unremitting and devoted attention to our interests and welfare, we have, we trust, not been forgetful of returning thanks to the Great Director of Hearts, that it has pleased him to furnish you with abilities so suitable, and a heart so warm in the labours with which you have been so long engaged.

To enumerate all the beneficial results which have accrued to ourselves and families from your exertions would, we feel, be taking up more room than the compass of this address will admit. We cannot avoid, however, expressing our belief that the name, which, as a body of workmen, we have obtained for general regularity and order, has arisen in consequence of our having in some degree followed the example and oft repeated precepts which you have so zealously set before us. We are perfectly convinced that you do not require any inducement to continue your labours in our midst, beyond that strong wish to benefit your fellow creatures, but in obedience to our own feelings, we have resolved upon begging your acceptance of a small memorial of our deep-rooted esteem for you.

In conclusion, we beg leave to express our utmost satisfaction with the open, straightforward, and manly manner in which you have, at all times treated us, and contributed to our comfort, and in the language of our noble Welsh adage, transacted all business between master and man 'in the Sun's face, and in the eye of light'.

With every feeling of gratitude and respect, we cordially invoke the Blessing of Heaven on you and yours for all future time.

Ynyspenllwch.
12th May 1866

If the sentiments expressed in the testament are a true reflection of the feelings of his colleagues, Mr. Griffiths was a gentleman well-respected by both master and servants.

Apart from ambitious personnel, tinplate workers usually were loath to move from their traditional home districts to obtain alternative employment within the trade. In a number of cases entire families— father, mother, children, even grandchildren—had secured employment in one works and so a strong affinity developed between masters and servants, especially if the latter had given good service. The advent of trades unionism in the second half of the nineteenth century forced workers to choose between union membership with its inherent allegience to fellow workers, and their continued loyalty to the firm which had provided them with employment and security in past years. This dichotomy of the tinplate workers loyalty continued until the early part of the twentieth century when improvements in employment conditions secured by the unions, especially over sensitive matters such as the rates of pay and the frequency of payments, convinced the vast majority of workers that more was to be gained from fraternalism than paternalism.

Throughout the duration of the eighteenth century and for a substantial part of the nineteenth, the customary method of wages payment was the 'contract' or 'group' system under which an experienced millman or tinman contracted with either the employer or his agent to produce an agreed amount over a specified period of time, usually one month. The millman (or tinman) then assembled his crew and set about honouring his part of the contract. Upon completion of the allotted work, he received the contracted sum out of which he in turn paid each member of his crew an agreed share.[21] The following payments to John Jenkins, a tinman, recorded in the cash book of the Caerleon Works for 1760 gives an indication of the gross pay for the weekly outputs achieved by Jenkins's crew, probably consisting of three or, at the most, four men.

20th May	25 boxes at 2/4d (11½p) per box = £2.18.4d. (£2.92½d)
27th May	18 boxes at 2/4d (11½p) per box = £2.02.0d. (£2.10p.)
3rd June	17 boxes at 2/4d (11½p) per box = £1.19.8d. (£1.98p)
10th June	23 boxes at 2/4d (11½p) per box = £2.13.8d. (£2.68p)
17th June	32 boxes at 2/4d (11½p) per box = £3.14.8d. (£3.73p)
1st July	26 boxes at 2/4d (11½p) per box = £3.00.8d. (£3.03p)
8th July	33 boxes at 2/4d (11½p) per box = £3.17.0d. (£3.85p)
15th July	31 boxes at 2/4d (11½p) per box = £3.12.4d. (£3.61½p)
22nd July	27 boxes at 2/4d (11½p) per box = £3.03.0d. (£3.15p)
29th July	35 boxes at 2/4d (11½p) per box = £4.01.8d. (£4.08p)[22]

Of course, arrangements such as these were open to abuse and there may well be an element of truth in the tale of the millman who, after having received his contracted remuneration on the last working shift of his monthly contract, immediately prevailed upon the members of his team to accompany him to the nearest ale-house at which his declared intention was to pay each individual his share. Instead, he plied them with beer until they were totally inebriated, the temporary loss of their faculties presenting him with the opportunity to abscond with the balance of their pay having spent no more than a very small proportion on the purchase of ale. Although this was untypical, workers in the industry welcomed the introduction of the system of direct payments by employers to all grades which, because of its popularity, reached a state of common application within the trade by the middle period of the nineteenth century.

Whilst it was recognised as a significant improvement on the 'contract' system, the arrangement under which individual workers agreed their conditions of employment by means of direct negotiation with the employer or his agent was a long way from being satisfactory. Because they held the balance of power, employers could dictate the terms of employment which consequently favoured them rather than their employees. This is exemplified by reference to the frequency of wages payments. Initially, it was monthly, though it was an accepted practice to pay an 'on account' amount (or 'sub' as it was commonly called) after two weeks. At the Melingriffith (Cardiff), the Copper Miners (Cwmavon) and the Upper Forest and Worcester Works at Morriston, the 'sub' was given in the form of credit at the company shop—'sop y gwaith'—a practice which not only held the employees to ransom (there were cases in which employees were dismissed for their non-patronization of the shop) but also minimised the cash requirement of the works and increased the overall profitability of the firm. Similarly, workers employed by companies in which local retailers had acquired shares were well advised to trade in their stores. Shopkeepers in the Neath and Briton Ferry areas in particular viewed investment in local tinplate firms as a means of boosting turnover at their retail establishments as well as, hopefully, securing a return on their investment.[23]

The deliberate underpayment of wages against the outputs achieved and the unilateral deductions from wages for spoilt work, alleged or authentic, by unscrupulous masters aggrieved the workers. It was a consequence of the need for an easily understandable aid to assist tinplate workers with little or no mathematical knowledge to check the accuracy of their wages that William Lewis, a pioneer of the trade union movement within the trade, produced in 1876 his 'Tinman's Companion', the first in a series of ready reckoners specifically compiled for use within the trade.

Lewis was born in Gwarycaeau, Port Talbot, in 1838 and spent all his formative years in the Afan district, hence the pseudonym 'Lewys Afan' bestowed on him by his Welsh compatriots. In 1871, a small group of tinplate workers gathered at the Bird-in-Hand Public House in Swansea to discuss the formation of an association which, by the unity of its members, could offer a measure of protection for those employed in the trade against the vagaries of the masters. The principal protagonists were Williams Lewis and Jenkin Thomas (Llew or Llewellyn) of Aberdulais. What they advocated evidently caught the imagination of their colleagues present at the meeting for out of the gathering was formed 'The Independent Association of Tinplate Makers' with Thomas as its President and Lewis as its Secretary. Although the Association, which soon gained ground in West Wales (the East Walians preferring the North of England based Amalgamated Malleable Ironworkers Union), was preceded by a localised and rather informal organisation established at Ystalyfera in 1868 with James Williams as its Secretary, it was the first distinctly Welsh trade union. Branch meetings were conducted in the native language and the minutes of the meetings and correspondence between the branches were recorded likewise.[24]

The level of contributions was set deliberately low at 7d (3p) per month in keeping with the exclusively 'protectionist' function of the union. Offering support to members who opposed enforced lay-offs or wage reductions, funds were accumulated for no other reason than to give a measure of financial support to workers involved in disputes with their employers over what was construed as unreasonable action on the past of the latter. Unlike a number of its contemporaries, the union remained outside the genus of 'friendly societies' whose principal purpose was the collection of monies from working members for redistribution to those unable to work because of sickness, accident or trade recession.

Notwithstanding the fact that its constitution precluded the pursuit of improvements in terms and conditions of employment, by 1874 the union claimed a membership of 4000 concentrated within the Swansea area. Many workers rejected union membership for fear of retribution from the employers, a fear that turned to reality for some of the more active members who were forced out of the trade in South Wales for reason of their pursuit of the extension of the union's spheres of influences. Even before the era of unionism, opposition to concerted action by workers, if only to prevent a lowering of their standard of living, came not only from the employers but also sometimes from quite unexpected sources. Throughout the length and breadth of Wales in the nineteenth century, non-conformity had captured the imagination of the disadvantaged members of the working class. This principally, although not exclusively, was their religion as was the established church that of their masters; through it they found a means of expression and a sense of identity. Those who administered the ministry were venerated by their congregations. Their word was the word of God even if it meant increased adversity and servility. Men of peace they may have been but radicals determined to rid the world of injustice they were not always, especially if that meant standing alongside members of their flock in confrontation with the employers. Amongst them were those who rejected and condemned the concept of concerted action against employers and by doing so often weakened the resolve of the labour force to stand firm against injustice. When, for example, a large number of tinplate workers gathered together at Swansea in 1834 to discuss their employers' insistence on implementing a reduction in wages, the Reverend Thomas Davies, Minister of the Pentre Chapel in the town, hastened to the spot and addressed the men, advising them to be patient under the existing difficulties and to remain loyal to their masters. With due reverence and respect, the Minister's words were heeded and the meeting broke up peacefully. Because of the religious obedience of the tinplate workers, on this occasion the masters seemed to have gained the upper hand.[25]

Inevitably, the determination of wage rates by direct negotiation between the employer and individual workers produced wide differences in the rates of pay between districts and even between works within districts. At Cardiff's Melingriffith Works in 1768, a Rollerman was contracted to work for the rate of 1 shilling and 3 pence (6p) per box and a Tinner for 1 shilling and 10 pence (9p) per box. Between 1759 and 1761 the comparative rates at the Caerleon Works in the East Wales district were 1 shilling and 6 pence (7½p) for rolling and 2 shillings and 4 pence (11½p) for tinning. In both cases the Rollerman and Tinman were responsible for paying the wages of their subordinate crewmen out of the gross earnings which, in the case of the Rollerman at Melingriffith, would not have exceeded £7.20p per week (120 boxes at 6p per box). With four men to a crew, the average payment per man would have been in the order of £1.08p for a working week of 72 hours i.e. 6 days of 12 hours per day.[26]

Generally, tinplate workers in West Wales worked for lower wage rates than their eastern district counterparts. Before 1874, individual tinmen in the east were paid 3 pence (1.25p) a box compared with the 2½ pence (1p) per box paid to the majority of tinmen in the western area.[27] The difference principally reflected both the greater demand for labour in the east, where tinplate works owners had to compete for their workers with the vast manpower requirements of the iron masters of Blaenavon, Tredegar, Ebbw Vale etc., and the influence on the area of the few tinplate works in the English Midland region where the rates paid were even higher than those of East Wales. Migrant labour not only brought news of these higher rates to the workmen of Wales but also of the success achieved by the new unions in England in bringing about improvements in the pay and conditions of workers.

Throughout the early eighteen-seventies the workers of the western area increasingly sought comparability with their colleagues in the east. Reflecting the aspirations of its members, Lewys Afan's Independent Association of Tinplate Workers in 1872 changed from being a passive organisation into one which actively pursued higher wages and other benefits from the employers. Later in that year, a delegation from the union presented the demands of the workmen to the masters and in reporting back to the members at a meeting in Aberavon stated that 'whilst received in a conciliatory spirit by some of the masters many had refused to consider them at all'.[28] The leaders of the Association—described as being 'volatile in temperament and more adept at agitation than negotiation'[29]—continued to press their demands for parity of rates in the belief that the masters would readily concede, given the good trading conditions and the shortage of skilled labour that existed at the time. But the employers of Carmarthenshire and Glamorganshire had other ideas and soon realised that unified resistance was essential. Separate regional Manufacturers' Associations that had been formed in 1873 were united by means of an amalgamation that took effect from 23rd March 1874. With membership covering thirty-one out of the then thirty-five works in the district, the majority of the manufacturers gave the union positive notice of their homogeneity and intention to ride out the storm.

Against the background of deteriorating market conditions, in February 1874 the union submitted formal claims for (a) recognition of their status and (b) parity of rates with their eastern colleagues to the owners of the Kidwelly Works. Soon after, similar submissions were made at a number of other works to which the employers immediately responded by terminating the contracts of all those employed at the works at which claims had been presented. They also undertook to refuse employment at non-union establishments to any worker unable to produce a discharge note from his previous employer. Furthermore, in a move designed to curtail outputs and stocks to levels more in keeping with the then reduced demand for tinplate, workers at the operating works had their working week cut by one-third from six to four days.

With attitudes hardening on both sides (so determined were the owners to maintain their unity that they agreed that any one amongst them breaking ranks to negotiate a separate agreement with the work-people would be obliged to pay £500 to a local charity), all tinplate works in the locality, apart from the Upper Forest and Worcester Works at Morriston whose owner, Edward Bagot, supported the men, and a few works in Llanelli, were closed by early May at the instigation of the owners. Mass meetings of the 'locked-out' work-people, addressed by the union's officials and supported by speeches from the leaders of the recently formed Collier's Union were held in Aberavon, Briton Ferry, Swansea and Llanelli. One such meeting held on open ground near to the Ivorites Arms Public House at Landore, Swansea was a preliminary to a march through the town. Addressing those assembled for the march, Jenkin Thomas advised them to behave 'fel bonheddigion' (like gentlemen), ostensibly to ensure public support. Dressed in their Sunday best, the march participants, carrying banners declaring the aims of the union and complimentary remarks to Mr. Bagot of the Upper Forest and Worcester Works, moved off to the sounds of four brass bands and a drum and fife ensemble.

After passing through Swansea, the procession made its way over the four miles to Morriston where the marchers re-assembled at the Bush Inn. After a while, Mr. Bagot himself arrived in a horse drawn wagon accompanied by the officials of the union.

Upon sighting the conveyance, a number of march participants moved forward enthusiastically, unhitched the horses and manually

180

William Lewis (Lewys Afan), General Secretary, The Independent Association of Tinplate Makers, 1871-87.

Coun. Ivor H. Gwynne, J.P., General Secretary, Tin and Steel Millmen's Association, 1904-21.

Thomas Phillips (Twm Phil), General Secretary, South Wales, Monmouthshire and Gloucestershire Tinplate Workers' Union, 1887-98; Tin and Sheet Millmen's Association, 1898-1904.

hauled the wagon to a nearby field where further exhortations were delivered by the union leaders. Later, as the crowd passed the residence of Mr. Bagot, each person was handed portions of bread and cheese and directed to a fresh water stream to quench their thirst. The bands continued to play, accompanying the songs and hymns of the gathered throng all sung in Welsh except for one in English as a tribute to the generosity and support of Mr. Bagot. Before the dispute the latter had been the Chairman of the Glamorgan Association of Tinplate Manufacturers; he resigned from the post after disagreeing with his fellow manufacturers over what he considered to be their premature and unwarranted action in locking out some twenty thousand tinplate workers.

One month later, approaches were made to the employers to re-open negotiations on a revised claim from the union but these, too, were rejected with the owners even spurning a suggestion of a reference to arbitration.

Faced with this disappointment and the total exhaustion of their hard-come-by savings, the out-of-work men resorted to begging from door to door to obtain food for their families—a totally demoralising act for the proud tinplate workers. The union itself, seemingly unprepared for such a lengthy dispute, soon ran into financial difficulties. With little funds at their disposal the exasperated officials appealed to their East Wales colleagues for support, but it seems that whatever assistance came from that source was of little substance. By July the union had lost effective control over its members and a drift back to work had begun. The first group to break the strike was the thousand-strong work-force at the Landore Tinplate Works when, by means of a ballot, they accepted a proposition to return to work at the old rates of pay. Seizing the opportunity to publicise the event, the first pay-out to the strike-breakers following their return to work was organised in a celebratory manner by the employers who hired a brass band to play whilst the workers filed into and out of the pay office, harvesting the fruits of their disloyalty.

Undoubtedly, this action on the part of the Landore men was the water-shed for the rest of the workmen whose support for the Association up until then had been unwavering. A few days later at a meeting held at Cwmbwrla (Swansea), William Lewis attempted to resuscitate enthusiasm for the cause but was vilified by the wives of the men locked-out and the meeting broke up in disarray. Others quickly followed the example of the Landore men and soon all works had re-opened, the return to work having taken place on the terms laid down by the masters.[30]

Notwithstanding this defeat, all was not completely lost by the union. The employers, having reflected on the aspirations of the workforce, eventually recognised and accepted the logic of a common scale of payments for all grades employed within the works of the western district. A proposal presented to the representatives of the work-people was discussed in a new spirit of co-operation and agreement was finally reached on 24th November 1874 on the following rates of pay which, although not implemented until 4th January 1875, became known within the trade as the '1874 List'.

COMPARISON OF WAGE RATES PRE AND POST THE '1874 LIST'

(Source: Hancocks H., *History of Tinplate Manufacture in Llanelli* and documents in Author's Collection)

GRADE OF LABOUR	PRE 1874 LIST RATE PER DOZEN BOXES		1874 LIST RATE PER DOZEN BOXES
	Melyn Works (Neath)	Morfa Works (Llanelli)	
Roller	3/2 (16p)	3/5.1/2d (17p)	3/5 (17p)
Doubler	2/6 (121/2p)	3/5/1/2d (17p)	3/5 (17p)
Furnaceman	2/3d (11p)	2/5.1/2d (12p)	2/7d (13p)
Behinder	1/0d (5p)	1/1.1/2d (5½p)	1/3d (6p)
Shearer	N/A	N/A	1/1d (5½p)
			RATE PER 100 BOXES
Annealers			
Coal	N/A	N/A	11/6d (57½p)
Gas	N/A	N/A	10/6 (52½p)

As the '1874 List' effectively levelled out the previously varying rates of pay it was welcomed enthusiastically by the men in the establishments where the rates formerly paid were below the norm but accepted with reluctance by those who earlier had enjoyed higher rates. Nonetheless, the principles governing the method of payment to tinplate workers established by the '1874 List' were to remain in force throughout the lifetime of the hand mill plants.

But even before the consolidation of wage rates under the 1874 Agreement, the performance-based system of payment commonly applied throughout the trade provided tinplate workers with potential earnings levels which compared favourably with those of other industrial occupations. In 1874, *The Cambrian* newspaper published the average weekly earnings of tinplate workers, quoting £2.00 For Rollerman, £1.75 for Doublers, whilst the Furnacemen received £1.50, the Behinders £0.75 and Grease Boys, £0.65 at a time when the average wage of adult male workers in the United Kingdom was but £0.95 per week.[31]

Despite the undoubted success of the 1874 Agreement, the Independent Association of Tinplate Workers never gained the comprehensive support it so badly needed to operate effectively. Its leaders, Jenkin Thomas and William Lewis, whilst fired with enthusiasm, were inexperienced and often failed to perceive the way in which market conditions influenced the attitude of the employers when the latter responded to claims presented for improved conditions of employment. Also, their inability to discern the underlying reasons for the workers' agitation on the one hand and the employers' obduracy on the other frequently distanced them from both groups.

Membership fluctuated with trade conditions, i.e. it increased when trade was at a low ebb and the threat of short-time working or dismissals heightened and fell with a buoyant market when employment and high earnings opportunities were at their peak. With the Association's income entirely dependent on the membership, it never achieved financial stability. Because of its monetary misfortunes and the fact that recognition by the employers was never fully secured it became defunct in 1887, the year in which Lewys Afan died, almost destitute, for his was a labour of love. He was interred in the cemetery of Babell Chapell, Cwmbwrla, Swansea, where a monument to him was erected by those whom he served so diligently.

Significant amongst the factors that caused the demise of the Independent Association of Tinplate Workers was its failure to become widely accepted across all districts making up the South Wales tinplate community. In East Wales, disaffection had always been evident with many tinplaters initially joining and then withdrawing from the union. But even when Lewys Afan's union was at its zenith the majority of the East Walians preferred to associate with their iron-working brethren in the English-based National

Amalgamated Association of Ironworkers whose General Secretary, John Kane, rather caustically commented in the following manner on the 1874 dispute organised by the Independent Association of Tinplate Workers:

> They have organised a dispute in their trade which has lasted some time and which is likely to give the employers an easy victory . . . Their past history is another proof that when there are two associations in the same trade the one weakens the other and the employers profit by the division.[32]

However, as with Lewys Afan's Association, John Kane's ironworkers union evidently could not sustain its activities within the tinplate trade for after 1876 no reference is made in its records to any branches in Wales.

Matters of common interest that arose at the workplace during the seventh and eighth decades of the eighteenth century invariably were dealt with at works or district level. Consequently, lack of unity amongst the workers from all districts weakened any effort to secure wholly justifiable improvements in conditions. For example, the practice adopted by certain masters of engaging juveniles as apprentices for work in the tinhouse, paying them below union rates during their apprenticeship and dismissing them when they reached the age at which the payment of adult rates was compulsory (i.e. 21 years), was abhorred throughout the trade, but action in opposition to the practice, known as the 'twopenny touch', was confined to the workmen of Morriston.

Within a few months of Lewys Afan's death a new union sprang up within the trade, principally as a consequence of events in Monmouthshire. In the second half of 1886 employers in the district sought to introduce a 10% reduction in the rates paid to their workers. The latter's resistance to the proposition resulted in them being 'locked out' of their places of employment. Delegates from the area visited the west and addressed works and district conferences for the purpose of enlisting support for their stance. Their mission achieved some success in that their West Wales colleagues agreed to assist in the raising of funds by the imposition of a levy on all those in full-time employment within the trade in their region. The amount of the levy varied from district to district; in Llanelli it was two shillings (10p) per man per week, whilst the workmen of Morriston and Pontardulais agreed to contribute, respectively, 5% and 7½% of their weekly wages to the fund. However, apathy amongst the workmen and inadequate administrative arrangements curtailed the effectiveness of the exercise and only a small amount of money actually reached those in need in Monmouthshire.

Despite this setback, which again emphasised the fragmented nature of the union movement within the trade, the regular contact between the tinplaters of the three counties of Monmouthshire, Glamorganshire and Carmarthenshire, established as a consequence of the dispute, augured well for the creation of a composite organisation to represent the interests of all tinplate workers, irrespective of location. Created in 1887 and registered early in the following year, the progeny of this new found affinity was an organisation entitled 'The South Wales, Monmouthshire and Gloucestershire Tinplate Workers' Union'. It differed from its predecessors in that membership was exclusive to those employed in tinplate works—iron and steel workers were specifically excluded under its Constitution. Unlike those of the Independent Association of Tinplate Workers, the officials of the new organisation were clear about its function from the very beginning—it existed to secure improved conditions of employment for tinplate workers from their employers. Payments were to be made: (a) to members on strike (which could take place only with executive approval) or locked-out as a consequence of the Union's pursuance of claims or (b) to those victimised i.e. dismissed by their employer for union activities. According to the rules of the union, any member qualifying for benefits would be paid at the sum of twelve shillings (60p) per week plus one shilling (5p) per child when on strike or locked out and fifteen shillings (75p) per week plus one shilling (5p) for each child when subjected to victimisation. Boys would be paid six shillings (30p) per week in the former case and seven shillings and six pence (37½p) per week if victimised. Weekly contributions to the union's funds initially amounted to six pence (2½p) for men and half that amount for boys.

Under the presidency of Thomas Benjamin of Abercarn and with Thomas Phillips (Twm Phil) as its first secretary, membership grew rapidly and within the space of twelve months the funds accumulated amounted to over £2,000. With ninety percent of tinplate workers in the western area being monoglot Welshmen, its notices were printed both in Welsh and in English and the proceedings at Union meetings in this district were similarly held and reported in both languages. It was necessary therefore for the officials of the Union to be bilingual.

Having been launched at a time of expanding market conditions, the Union's primary objective was the re-establishment and thereafter the maintenance of the 1874 List, previously abandoned when the demand for tinplate had slumped during the early 1880's. Equally as important was the question of restricting the output per mill to thirty-six boxes per shift of eight hours. If the Union could successfully enforce this ruling it would force the employers to engage additional labour in order to satisfy their customers' requirements. Other matters of concern were:

(a) securing the payment of wages to employees on a weekly basis
(b) minimising the health hazards to which tinplate workers were exposed.
(c) the preferential payment of outstanding wages in the event of an employer's bankruptcy
(d) compensatory payments for the dependents of employees fatally injured or permanently incapacitated whilst at work.

The Union's first success was achieved in 1889 by its members employed at the six works in the Morriston district. Here the employers had been presented with a list of grievances that included the reinstatement of two men dismissed without notice and just cause, the promotion of workmen without due regard to seniority rules and, fundamentally, the re-application of the 1874 rates. A demonstration of support by some 7,000 to 8,000 tinplate workers from all areas, east and west, held in the town gave encouragement to the local workmen in their campaign. This display of unity obviously had the desired effect on the employers of the district who, unwilling to suffer a stoppage of work at a time of prosperity for the trade, hastily agreed to participate in an arbitration reference on the workers demands. Upon consideration of the cases presented by both sides the arbitration committee, composed of representatives of the employers and the workmen, accepted the arguments of the Union. Encouraged by this success, the Union subsequently sought and gained the re-establishment of the 1874 List throughout the industry. Similarly, the 'thirty-six boxes per shift' rule again became effective within the trade.

Following their early successes the officers of the Union recognised the need to improve their methods of communication as the membership was spread throughout an area consisting of, roughly, 1,400 square miles. Whilst transportation difficulties restricted the movement of the officials, especially to the works in the outlying districts, the printed word could convey the same message as would an official on a personal visit. The use of this medium of communication would allow the up-until-then largely peripatetic full-time Union officer more time to devote to essential matters such as seeking improvements in members' conditions of employment. The manifestation of this concept was the *Industrial World*, a daily publication exclusive to the South Wales tinplate industry in which matters pertaining to the trade and the affairs of the Union were reported as well as local, national and international news. By 1889, branches of the Union were to be found in seventy-six out of the then eighty-five works in South Wales and over the next three years its membership increased to 10,000 out of the 25,000 employed in the trade. Before long, however, this period of growth was to come to an end. The introduction of the McKinley Tariff decimated the lucrative American export market and soon (i.e. by 1895) between 10,000 and 12,000 tinplaters were unemployed with 6,550 having been idle for almost two years. This depressing state of affairs continued unabated over the succeeding years and by 1898 the number of registered tinplate workers had fallen to 16,000, some 10,000 less than the number registered at the beginning of the decade. Even those fortunate enough to enjoy employment on a fairly continuous basis had their wages, mainly based on outputs, reduced as a consequence of the fall in demand.[33]

Against the back-cloth of these difficult trading conditions, the employers sought and obtained a further curtailment of employment costs by means of a reduction in the rates paid, the extent of the reduction varying from works to works depending on how badly each enterprise was affected by the recession. The abrogation of the 'thirty-six boxes per shift' rule was also sought by the employers who believed that its strict application had contributed to the closure of a number of works in the Western area. Workmen rendered idle as a consequence of the recession paraded through the streets of Swansea displaying banners with slogans intended to induce a feeling of guilt amongst their colleagues who, by not upholding the rule, were in direct contravention of the Union's policy, which also included the maintenance of the 1874 List. A levy of 5% of earnings imposed by the Union on all members at work for the benefit of their unemployed colleagues failed to generate sufficient monies and so, in order to meet its commitment to the unemployed members, the Union resorted to the use of its accumulated funds which, consequently, soon became exhausted.

Dissenting voices were to be heard within the Union ranks over its policies. In 1893, workers at the Upper Forest and Worcester, Dyffryn and Beaufort Works in the Morriston district, hitherto considered to be a Union stronghold, contemplated withdrawing from the Tinplate Workers Union and establishing a locally based independent organisation. Whilst nothing came of this particular proposal, the Morriston men nonetheless agreed to distribute locally, instead of through the Union's central office, the monies generated by the imposition of the 5% levy within the district. With the disaffection spreading to other districts it was inevitable that the united resistance would soon be breached. The first group of workers to concede to the employers' demands were those employed at the South Wales Tinplate Works, Llanelli, when they agreed in December 1894 to a 10% reduction on the standard rates. A reduction of 12½% was subsequently accepted by workmen at Morriston but the employers' demand for the revocation of the thirty-six boxes per shift rule was met with stern resistance. This angered the employers of the district whose reaction was to close their establishments, locking out more than 3,000 workers.

With no means of support other than what little savings they may have accumulated, a long period of idlenes enforced on tinplate workers caused immeasurable distress within the community. Workmen, particularly those in the Llanelli area, despairing of the situation, pleaded with their masters to re-open their places of employment. Demoralised and dejected they agreed to the waiving of the 1874 List and to return to work for rates ranging between 10% and 22% below those contained in the List. In a last-ditch effort to re-assert its authority, in August 1895 the Union pursued the restoration of the 1874 List in works at Llanelli and Swansea with, it could claim, some success for by the early part of 1896 List rates were again observed at 270 out of the total of 510 mills in the trade. Lower rates were paid to the crews employed in 44 mills which left a total of just under 200 mills (representing approximately 40% of productive capacity) still idle. Fifty-five of these were in a position to be re-started immediately if the workmen accepted their employer's proposals for reductions in the rates payable. Although the officials thought otherwise, the observance of the 1874 List in over half the total number of mills was not solely the result of their efforts. Of greater influence was the reduction in capacity achieved by the partial or, as in some cases, the complete closure of works to accord with the lower level of demand. The majority of the establishments which continued in production were therefore operating at a level approaching capacity and it was their consequential profitability that allowed the owners to pay their employees the rates prescribed in the 1874 List.

Seeking to introduce an arrangement whereby the available work would be shared more equitably, the Union put forward a plan for periodic closures of all works. However, this strategy of 'a little for all' foundered because of the lack of uniformity in employees contracts, some being contracted to work on a daily basis, some week-by-week, whilst others were engaged on monthly contracts. By the end of 1896 an improvement in trading conditions facilitated the re-establishment of the 1874 List in almost all of the operating works. But again it was short-lived as a further fall-off in trade prompted the employers to seek wage reductions from the workmen of Monmouthshire, Glamorganshire and Gloucestershire. At a meeting of Union delegates from all districts an official recommendation that an across-the-board 15% reduction in the rates of pay be accepted was vehemently condemned by the representatives of the Briton Ferry district and the motion consequently failed. Later, the Briton Ferry district branch resolved to sever its connection with the Union—a move that hastened it's collapse.

Whilst contributory, the decision of the Briton Ferry men was not by itself the reason for the union's demise. Of greater significance was the effect of increased animosity between those employed in the two principal sections of the trade, viz. the millmen and the tinhousemen. A divergence of opinion had emerged during the eighteen-eighties at the time when the earliest attempts at manufacturing tinplate in America consisted of the application of a coating of tin onto blackplate imported from Britain. As a result, a number of tinhouse employees were rendered idle through lack of work whilst the millmen, who produced the blackplate for export, suffered no such effect. Of course, following the imposition of the McKinley Tariff the millmen were similarly affected, but the resentment of the tinhousemen over their colleagues earlier lack of support was deep rooted and precluded the restoration of a state of equanimity between the two factions.

The crisis within the Union worsened, the first casualty being its daily newspaper *The Industrial World* (then titled *The Daily Industrial World*) which ceased to be published after the 14th October, 1898 edition. In the next year, four hundred disaffected Morriston tinplaters (mainly tinhouse grades) left the Tinplate Workers Union and joined the influential Dockers' Union. Dissatisfaction also prevailed in the Llanelli district where a number of workers in tinplate establishments joined another general workers' union, The Gasworkers, following a recruitment campaign led by Will Thorne, its General Secretary. The millmen, wishing to maintain their association with a metal 'trade' union, joined the British Steel Smelters. By February 1899 the number of tinplate workers in membership of the Dockers' Union was assessed to be 2,500 whilst those in the Steel Smelters Union approached 2,000. Sandwiched between the national unions was the Tin and Sheet Millmen's Association, formed in 1899 with Twm Phillips, former secretary of the Tinplate Workers Union, as its Secretary and Ivor Gwynne as its President. The Tinplate Workers Union ceased to exist on 14th January 1899 when a conference of delegates held in Swansea decided by 2,000 votes to 565 to form separate societies for the millmen and tinhousemen.[34]

To Phillips, the thought of unions with interests outside of tinplate manufacture representing tinplate workers was anathema. His attitude accentuated the discordant relationship that had existed for some time between the Tinplate Workers Union and John Hodge's Steel Smelters arising out of the failure of the former to support the Smelters in a contest against the owners of the Pontymister Steel and Tinplate Works, near Pontypool, when the latter sought a reduction in wages. Determined to defeat the Smelters, the owners closed the steelmaking side of the business for a period of fourteen months between September 1893 and November 1894. The men employed in the tinplate section of the works, members of the Tinplate Workers Union, flagrantly rejected appeals for support and continued to work whenever required. Animosity between the two organizations increased in 1898 when approaches made by John Hodge to Phillips on the possibility of an amalgamation of interests were firmly rebuffed by the officials of the, by then, moribund Tinplate Workers Union. Even when the major unions acknowledged the speciality of the tinplate trade and agreed to the formation of separate sections for tinplate workers with substantial degrees of autonomy, Phillips remained obdurate and rejected the concept of a merger.

Ben Tillet (1860-1943) of the Dock Workers' Union.

John Hodge, General Secretary, British Steel Smelters, Mill, Iron, Tinplate and Kindred Trades Association, 1886-1918.

Workers employed in the tinplate trade consequently had the choice of joining any one of several unions. Four represented production grades viz. The Dock, Wharf, Riverside and General Workers Union, The British Steel Smelters, Mill, Iron and Tinplate Workers, The National Union of Gasworkers and General Labourers and The Tin and Sheet Millmens' Association. The Welsh Artisans Union offered membership to non-process workers and The Amalgamated Society of Engineers catered for the needs of craftsmen. Intensive recruiting by these organizations undoubtedly paid dividends for approximately 85% of the labour force was unionised by the beginning of this century. The success of the Dockers' Union over the Gas Workers Union in securing the allegiance of the majority of tinhouse and general tinplate workers was largely attributable to Tillet's oratorical powers and the efforts of local representatives such as James Wignall at Swansea.

The more realistic amongst the union leaders, especially the ebullient Ben Tillett of the Dockers' Union and the phlegmatic John Hodge of the Steel Smelters, soon reached an understanding on the question of the respective areas of representation. Their agreement confirmed the existing informal arrangement whereby the Steel Smelters represented the Millmen (Hot and Cold Mills), Openers, Picklers and Annealers, whilst the Dockers' Union embraced tinhouse, assorting and warehouse grades. Despite several further attempts at an amalgamation with the Steel Smelters, the Tin and Sheet Millmens' Association continued to represent Millmen in certain works and remained independent until 1922 when its unilateralism crumbled and it finally became part of The Iron and Steel Trades Confederation.[35]

The Dockers Union benefitted greatly from its representation of tinplate workers. At times, the scale of contributions to the Union's general fund from the tinplate branches was greater than those from other branches within the organisation. In 1908, for example, contributions from tinplate workers amounted to over £1,500, whilst the combined income from the London and Hull areas, both major ports but where Union activity had declined as a consequence of employer antagonism, was a meagre £155. Realising the importance of its tinplate trade membership, the Dockers' Union was not averse to allowing the high degree of local autonomy sought by its tinplate branches and so by 1910 three representatives of the tinplate trade sat on the Executive Council, whilst locally, a District Secretary had been appointed to serve exclusively the interests of tinplate workers.

However, this affinity of interests between unions did not extend into the political arena. In February 1900, the Dockers' Union at national level played not an insignificant role in the formation of the Labour Representation Committee whilst locally its officials encouraged the establishment of constituency parties. At Swansea, where several dock workers sat on the Town Council, Ben Tillet was asked to stand as the Labour candidate in the Parliamentary Election of 1910. His candidature, however, was not enthusiastically received by all tinplate workers, who, still mindful of the effects of the McKinley Tariff, backed the free trade policies of the Liberal Party. Tillet also drew criticism from tinplate workers during the campaign for forcing a three-cornered fight in the constituency to the disadvantage of the Liberal candidate, for disagreeing with Lloyd George's economic policies and, reflecting the strictly non-conformist attitude prevailing in the area, for holding political meetings on a Sunday. As one prominent tinplate representative was reported as saying:-

The workers of Wales were men of more deeply religious convictions than men of the same class in England. Fancy Mr. Tillet holding two political meetings on the Sunday.

So hostile were tinplate workers to Tillet's candidature that those in membership of the Dockers' Union threatened to resign. Despite the protests Tillet remained obdurate and stood at the election but his defeat was inevitable. However, even he must have been surprised at his lack of support from the electorate—the winning candidate, Alfred Mond, Liberal, receiving over four times as many votes as he had.[36]

The final decade of the nineteenth century was a turbulent period for the union movement within the tinplate trade. Recession had bitten deeply and the membership had fluctuated according to the needs and strength of the workforce. For the employers, too, this had been a time of great trauma. Many had gone out of business and those that had survived had only done so by cutting outputs, prices and profit margins. Competition between firms was fierce and uncompromising. The collapse in 1896 of the Employers Association, formed a little over twenty years previously, was perhaps inevitable under such

194

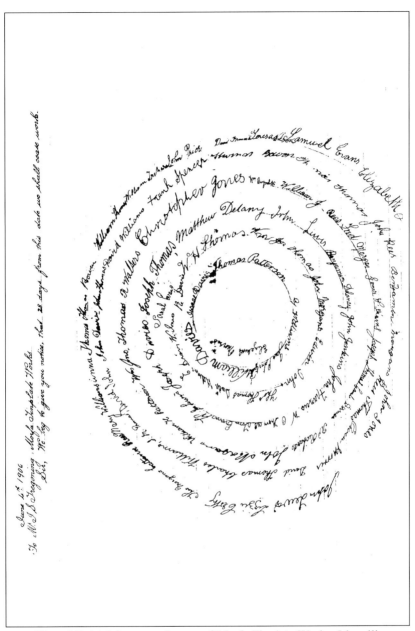

'Round Robin' from employees of Morfa Tinplate Works, Llanelli.

divisory circumstances. However, by 1899 the increasing strength of the trade union movement—a reflection of the up-turn in the market for tinplate and the effectiveness of experienced union leaders such as Tillet and Hodge—prompted the employers to unite again, this time under the aegis of 'The Welsh Plate and Sheet Manufacturers' Association'.

In all, thirty-six firms participated in the Association and its formation signified the first step towards the establishment of a formally constituted body providing for the bil-lateral examination of matters pertaining to the trade. Although the idea had first been mooted by a number of employers in the previous year, it was in fact Ben Tillet who became the leading protagonist for the establishment of a Joint Conciliation Board through which masters and men (or at least their representatives) could seek to resolve their differences. His propositioning of fellow trade-unionists representing tinplate workers to accept the concept met with some success as the foundations for joint negotiating and conciliation machinery soon were being laid down. At a meeting of the Joint Unions held in the Spring of 1899 the following resolution was passed:

That an immediate request be made to each employer as to his willingness to join an Association of Employers and that the foregoing societiesThe British Steel Smelters, Mill, Iron, Tinplate and Kindred Trades Association, The Dock, Wharf, Riverside and General Workers Union, The National Union of Gasworkers and General Labourers and The Tin and Sheet Millmen's Association also use all their energy to organise the workmen with the view to an alliance for the control of the trade both in regard to selling price and uniformity of wage rates and conditions, the unions pledging themselves to withdraw labour from those employers who do not join the employers' section of the Association, the associated employers on their part aiding the workmen by either finding work for such displacement of labour or aiding in a fund for their support during such enforced idleness. Further, that this conference urges the formation of a Joint Conciliation and Wages Board and that all matters in dispute be submitted to such board before any action is taken on either side.[37]

Clearly, the unions' initiative in passing this resolution was an acknowledgement of the advantages to be gained from the establish-

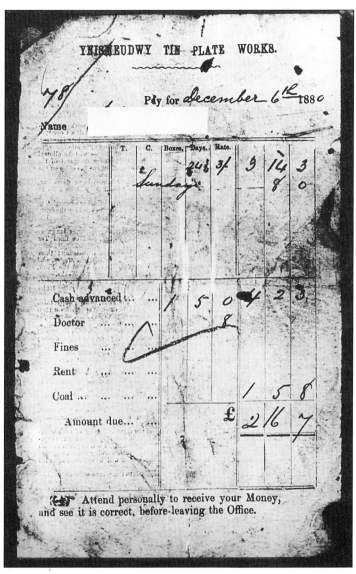

Pay docket, 6th December 1880, for employee (probably a craftsman) employed at the Ynysmeudw Tin Plate Works. Note the gross pay of £4.2.3d (£4.11p) for 24¾ days work, inclusive of premium for Sunday work and the advance of £1.5.0d (£1.25p) made halfway through the period.

ment of a joint body not only to regulate the relationships between master and servant but also to provide a vehicle for the discussion of matters of common interest pertaining to the trade. Without doubt, the wisdom of the leaders of the unions who were involved in the formation of the Joint Conciliation Board stood the test of time as no strike or lock-out of a comprehensive nature took place exclusively within the tinplate trade over the eight-five years from the time the Board first functioned in 1899 under the Chairmanship of Ernest Trubshaw of Llanelli, until it was wound up in 1984, having been superseded by the negotiating and disputes procedures operated on a corporate basis by the British Steel Corporation.

Initially, the Board, made up of fourteen representatives from each side, tackled the question of the great variety of pay rates applying within the trade following the abandonment of the 1874 List. Both sides recognised the benefits of a uniform pay rates structure and, as a consequence, the Standard List of rates was re-established with effect from 1st October 1899. Other events of significance associated with the Board throughout its existence are as follows:

1907 The Associated Society of Engineers (representing craftsmen) joined the Board.

1909 The Welsh Artisans Union (again representing craft employees) joined the Board.

1913 The Dockers' Union claimed a membership of 6000 within tinplate trade and the Employers' Side represented 80% of the then capacity within the trade.

1917 Anticipating the cessation of World War I hostilities, the Government of the day under the leadership of David Lloyd George established a Reconstruction Committee whose members were charged with the responsibility of preparing the ground for the peacetime re-habilitation of Britain's industrial base and social framework. A Sub-Committee of the Reconstruction Committee under the Chairmanship of the Right Hon. J.H. Whitley M.P. was asked to examine the means by which the conditions of employment for work people in the various trades and industries were determined, and to recommend improvements. It was a tribute to the wisdom and foresighted-ness of all those concerned with the Welsh tinplate industry that the Committee recommended the establishment of formally-constituted Joint Industrial Councils (known as

Whitley Councils after the Committee's Chairman) based on the rather informal (i.e. not statutorily recognised) arrangements governing employer/employee relations that had existed within the tinplate trade since 1899.

1918   Proposals adopted by the trades unions representing tinplate workers and by the Welsh Plate and Sheet Manufacturers' Association providing for the formation of a Joint Industrial Council for the whole of the Welsh tinplate trade.

1924   The title of the Board was changed to the Welsh Tinplate and Sheet Trades Joint Industrial Council.

1929   The Sliding Scale Agreement, by which wages were related to the profitability of the tinplate industry, came into force. An independent firm of chartered accountants factually ascertained the average basis selling price of tinplate from which was deducted the actual cost of steel and tin. The balance was translated to a percentage addition to base wage rates according to an agreed formula. The Agreement functioned until 1940.

1935   The Joint Industrial Council unsuccessfully endeavoured to establish a comprehensive superannuation scheme for all workers employed in the tinplate industry. The employers' side put up £50,000 to establish the fund and undertook to contribute 1¼d (½p) per basis box on the whole of their production. The workpeople were asked to contribute 2½% of their gross weekly wages but on a trade-wide ballot they rejected the scheme, 49½% voting in favour and 50½% against.

1939   The coming into production of the Ebbw Vale Works brought the first tinplate cold reduction plant in the United Kingdom under the jurisdiction of the Joint Industrial Council.

1941   The complete ban on the export of tinplate because of the Lease-Lend arrangements with U.S.A. forced the closure of 31 works and reduced the labour force from 24,000 to 10,000.

1950   The main concern of those involved with the industry after the War was the shortage of skilled labour. This was not resolved satisfactorily until 1950 when the Joint Industrial Council agreed on the recruitment and training of men who were to be brought over from Italy. Over the years 1950 to 1956, some 2,000 Italians were recruited to work in the hand mills.

1951   Trostre Works came into production and under the jurisdiction of the Board.

1952	Fifteen hand mill works permanently closed.
1956	Velindre Works came into production and under the aegis of the Board. By arrangement with the Joint Industrial Council the labour required for the manning of Trostre and Velindre was drawn—subject to suitability—from workmen employed in the hand mills plants.
1956/60	The remaining 25 hand mill works were closed permanently at intervals between 1956 and 1960.
1963	The Tinplate Trade Labour Fund, out of which £645,000 had been paid to 5,900 male and female workers, was wound up. The Fund had been established voluntarily by the Welsh Plate and Sheet Manufacturers' Association in October 1946 by a levy of 1d (½p) per basis box on the output of its members to provide for the payment of grants of assistance to workpeople whose employment was terminated as a result of the coming into production of the new continuous strip plants. The Fund was administered by Trustees and a Special Joint Sub-Committee, both appointed equally by the Employers' and Workmen's sides of the Council and preceded by two decades the State Redundancy Payments Scheme.
1970	The Welsh Plate and Sheet Manufacturers' Association was wound up and on 16th October, 1970 the title of the Joint Industrial Council was changed to the Welsh Tinplate Board and the constitution amended to provide for the appointment of the employers' representatives by the Tinplate Group of the Strip Mills Division of the British Steel Corporation instead of the Association.
1984	Welsh Tinplate Board wound up.

Without doubt, the importance of the Joint Conciliation Board in preserving, throughout its lifetime, a high degree of industrial harmony within the trade cannot be overstated. Disagreements arising between employers and employees, whether confined to a particular works or common to all sectors of the trade, were usually brought to an amicable conclusion before escalating into a stoppage of work or lockout. Both the employers and the trade unions involved were keen to see the Board not only survive but also grow in authority. In later years, the immeasurable consequences, both technical and social, of the transition from hand mills to strip processing could not have been dealt with in such an effective and humane manner had it not been for the respect that all concerned had for the long-established consultative arrangements operating within the framework of the Board.

Although at the beginning there existed a degree of enmity between the unions themselves over recognition rights, overall the progressive attitudes of the new generation of union leaders such as Tillet, Hodge and Griffiths and their counterparts of Trubshaw, Herbert Rees and Theodore Gibbins amongst the employers assisted considerably in the development of a sound platform for future employer/employee relations. Employers were not averse to the unions seeking to recruit members from amongst the work-force and, reciprocally, the unions brought pressure to bear on members employed in non-associated firms not to accept terms more favourable than those agreed within the Board. For example, the Board agreed to implement a week's stop during the 1906/7 Christmas/New Year period to bring the level of production more in line with the demand for tinplate. The non-aligned employers (at the Abercarn, Abertillery, Blaina, Melingriffith, Pontymister, Redbrook and Tynewydd works in East Wales and the Cwmfelin (Swansea) Works in West Wales), in seeking to gain an advantage over their colleagues affiliated to the Board, pressurised their workers to continue with the production of tinplate throughout the period. In consequence, the General Secretary of the Steel Smelters Union wrote to the union branches concerned in the following manner:

Your branch misapprehends the point of difference entirely. It is not a question of trade but a question of honour. Let me put it to you. The Conciliation Board was really instituted by our society—an Employers' Association naturally followed—and there can be no question of the fact that it has helped us in maintaining the List. Your firm left the Association because they desired to reap advantages that would not be obtained if inside the Employers' Association.

Let me beg of you to remember this—that notices had to be put in last summer to force your firm to pay the Association rates when they were cribbing sheets off you. Let me also remind you of the long agreement which your firm forced out of you when times were bad. In refusing or hesitating to act according to the request made to you, you are taking the side of your firm, who but for the society would reduce you as they have done before.

The honour and integrity of the society with respect to the pledges of your delegates are in your hands . . . the duty of your branch is plain—to be honourable to your society and its pledges.[38]

The Workmen's Side of the Board was particularly stringent in maintaining discipline within its own ranks. It insisted on its members not stopping work in furtherance of a dispute without just cause and before the expiration of the agreed period of notice to the employer. In 1909 the attention of the Workmen's Side had been drawn by the Secretary of the Employers' Side to a stoppage of work by members of the Tin and Sheet Millmen's Association at the Teilo Works, Pontardulais following a roll breakage in the mills. The Executive of the union expressed regret at the occurrence and instructed the then General Secretary, Ivor Gwynne, to immediately investigate the circumstances. Having met with the men, the Secretary reported them having admitted that their action had been unconstitutional and consequently they had agreed to an immediate return to work.

The authority of the Workmen's Side of the Board was further challenged in 1911, again by employees at the Teilo Works. On this occasion the employer had registered concern over the practice of young men employed as Behinders leaving the Works on the occasions when the mills unexpectedly came to a halt. Immediately, Ivor Gwynne was instructed by his Executive to write to the branch 'pointing out that should the Behinders leave the mills when a short stoppage takes place and not be at their posts when the mill is ready they (i.e. members of the Executive) would not be responsible for any action the Management or the Employers' Association may take in dealing with the same'.[39]

The firmness displayed by the unions in dealing with unconstitutional action was not confined to rebellious members. Obviously there were times when a firm stance needed to be taken in that dealings with the employers. However, in this respect the unions were not always successful. In 1902 for example, the Steel Smelters Union sought to change the method of wages computation applied in some works. With gauges (i.e. the thickness of the sheets) becoming thinner and the sheets lighter, grievances arose as a consequence of those whose earnings were based on the weight of material processed receiving less money than previously earned whilst those paid by area (i.e. by box) benefitted financially from the change. An agreement providing for all grades, excepting craftsmen, to have their earnings based on area (i.e. a standard 'Basis Box' of tinplate comprising 31360 square inches or 112 sheets, each 20 inches by 14 inches), became effective in June 1903. At first, this new arrangement was not universally accepted as some groups of workers argued that appropriate allowances should also be given for extraordinarily heavy or large sheets (e.g. Canadas—large sheets used mainly for roofing— or 'doubles'). Extensive negotiations within the Board on the issue failed to produce an early resolution and so both sides agreed to invoke the arbitration stage in procedure.

The debate continued over the question of establishing appropriate terms of reference for the arbitration but again to no avail. The employers, frustrated with the failure of the Union to exert authority over a minority of their members, decided to bring the matter to a head by closing the works concerned. By September 1903 about 14,000 workers were locked out and within a week the Union, realising that the issue concerned but a small proportion of the workforce employed mainly in Monmouthshire, accepted the proposed terms of reference for arbitration. Having received and examined the arguments of both sides, the Arbitrator, Sir Kenneth Digby of the Board of Trade, found in favour of the employers, a decision that the Union accepted graciously, if reluctantly, as it meant that in return for the payment of wages based on area with some, if little, compensation for the heavier gauges of sheet it was required to abandon the hitherto customary restriction on output of thirty-six boxes per shift.

Following the removal of this almost traditional constraint on the rate of production, output per mill increased from an average of 500 boxes per week to about 750 boxes per week—a level which both the employers and unions alike appreciated could not be further improved without the provision of extra labour. Nonetheless, the output potential of mills in tinplate works in Germany, Russia and particularly the USA exceeded that of the Welsh mills because of a combination of more modern equipment and higher manning levels. Mill crews consisted of five men in Germany, seven in Russia and either eight or nine in America, compared with the four men per mill in Wales. Apart from Germany, the labour productivity of the Welsh works in the period immediately preceeding the First World War compared unfavourably with other tinplate manufacturing countries but this had more to do with the technology employed than the efforts of the millmen.

COMPARATIVE PRODUCTIVITY PERFORMANCES PRE 1914

(Sources: 1913 Reports by T. Griffiths and S. Jones of the Steel Smelters Union and I.H. Gwynne of The Tin and Sheet Millmen's Association).

COUNTRY	NO. OF MEN PER MILL	AVERAGE OUTPUT (BOXES) PER SHIFT OF 8 HOURS	AVERAGE OUTPUT PER MANSHIFT (BOXES)
Wales	4 (6)	45 (62/75)	11.25 (10.33/12.5)
Germany	5	45	9.00
Russia	7	95/100	13.57/14.28
USA	8/9	100/110	c 12.50

N.B. The figures in brackets illustrate the labour productivity in Wales following the introduction of the 1st and 2nd Helpers into the Mill crew.

It is noticeable from the above table that the productivity of the Welsh workers was not too far adrift from the American mill crews, even though the latter consisted of double the number of men working in modern factories incorporating the best equipment and offering superior ergonomic working conditions by comparison with the 'sweat shops' of South Wales. In the Russian works (the Moscow Metal Works) which had Welshmen in all the senior jobs, the higher output per manshift principally resulted from the installation of additional equipment, viz. three furnaces instead of the two per mill in Wales, and more powerful engines (diesel and electric driven) providing 800 h.p. and 46 revolutions per minute in contrast to the steam powered engines of between 400 and 600 h.p. that drove the Welsh mills at 30 to 36 r.p.m. When all these factors are taken into account the physical performance of the Welsh millmen was considerably higher when compared with that of their overseas counterparts.

Additional labour in the mills was first discussed in 1913 and although both sides then agreed to increase the mill crew manning by two (viz. the 1st and 2nd Helpers) the implementation of the change was deferred until 1920 because of the shortage of manpower created by the Great War. The introduction of the two Helpers went someway towards placating the millmen following the employers' rejection of the Union's (the British Steel Smelters, Mill, Iron, Tinplate and Kindred Trades Association) request for the number of men per crew to equate to the American 'double manning' arrangement. With the two additional Helpers, a single mill crew, consisting of six men, was capable of producing between 1,000 and 1,200 boxes per week (62 to 75 boxes per shift) compared with the maximum of 750 boxes per week possible from a four man crew.

Although its introduction was rejected by the workmen themselves in 1920, on several occasions during the nineteen-twenties the unions resurrected the proposal to introduce shifts lasting six hours instead of the customary eight. Unemployment amongst tinplate workers had risen to alarming levels and the unions, in seeking a means of creating more jobs, believed that the answer lay in a shorter working week. Eventually, a scheme for work-sharing was determined by the Joint Industrial Council but, although agreed in 1934, its application was not mandatory and consequently little progress was made in implementing it before 1937. Resistance came from both sides; from the workers (especially those at Gorseinon) for fear of its effect on seniority positions and from the employers who worried about the effect that the introduction of an additional crew (i.e. four crews working 6 hour shifts were required to cover 24 hours compared with the three crews working 8 hours stints) would have on production costs and the quality of the product. The concern over the quality effect was founded on the disturbance that would occur to established crews when making up the fourth crew, having regard to promotional arrangements based on seniority and the injection of newly-recruited employees into the lower, but nonetheless important, jobs in the hierarchy. Lincoln Evans, then Assistant General Secretary of the Iron and Steel Trades Confederation (himself a former tinplate worker), condemned the attitude of the dissenters amongst his members. Concerted efforts by the leaders of the unions concerned, i.e. Lincoln Evans and Ernest Bevin of the Transport and General Workers Union (formerly the Dockers Union), undoubtedly paid dividends as the pace of the introduction of work-sharing schemes quickly gathered momentum throughout 1938, especially in the Morriston and Briton Ferry areas. By 1939, at least 58 works within the trade operated six-hour shift systems. The practice was short-lived, however, as the shortages of manpower brought about by the onset of World War II made the six-hour stint impossible to operate and all works soon re-introduced the eight-hour shift.

In keeping with national trends, unions representing tinplate workers from time-to-time applied pressure on the employers to reduce the total number of hours worked each week. Before 1899 the hours worked amounted to 72 in one week (six shifts of 12 hours per shift) followed by 60 hours in the next week (five shifts of 12 hours each) giving an average of 66 hours over the fortnight. Saturday afternoons and Sundays were not usually worked but given over to maintenance of the equipment. By 1914 only a few mills, mainly those powered by water, still held to the 12 hour shift, the introduction of the eight-hour shift having commenced in some works before the turn of the century. Initially, the eight-hour shift system produced a working week averaging 43.33 hours i.e. from the 6 a.m. to 2 p.m. shift on Monday, the first shift of the week during which the rolls were changed, turned and warmed prior to the commencement of production which then continued through the week until 4.00 p.m. on Saturday. After World War I most of the works introduced a noon Saturday finish, bringing the working week for shiftmen down to an average of 42 hours i.e. 15 shifts of eight hours plus six hours on a Saturday, rostered over three weeks. Dayworkers, including craftsmen, remained at work for the much longer period of 54 hours each week made up of six stints each of nine hours from Monday to Saturday. Sunday work, much abhorred by tinplaters, if ever necessary, was undertaken on an overtime basis. After the 1939-44 War the hours of work of daymen were reduced gradually to match those of the shiftmen.

In the early days, when earnings were entirely related to performance, the wages of tinplate workers fluctuated according to variations in the level of demand for the product. The frequent closing and re-opening of the Beaufort Works in Morriston, reflecting periods of trade recession and buoyancy, gained for it the affectionate name of the 'Umbrella Works' amongst the citizens of the town. Weather conditions, too, affected the earnings of tinplate workers; on particularly hot and humid days it proved impossible for employees to carry out their gruelling tasks for the whole of the shift whilst in works entirely dependent on water power drought in summer or the icing up of machinery and feeder streams in winter brought production to a halt.

Notwithstanding the factors which could inhibit their earnings potential, generally the wages of tinplate workers compared favourably when demand for tinplate was good with those of employees in other industries. A survey of the weekly earnings of tinplate workers undertaken in 1906 found wages averaging from £1.2.9. (£1.12p.) for labouring grades to £3.2.10. (£3.14p.) for Rollermen. The earnings of all the grades covered by the survey are identified in the following table:

AVERAGE WEEKLY EARNINGS OF SOUTH WALES (INCLUDING GLOUCESTER) FULL-TIME ADULT (I.E. 20 YEARS AND OVER) MALES

(Sources: *Report of Enquiry by the Board of Trade into the Earnings and Hours of Labour of Workpeople in the U.K.*, Comd. 5814 1906).

GRADE OF LABOUR	METHOD OF PAYMENT	AVERAGE WEEKLY EARNINGS	
		£ s. d.	£. p.
Furnaceman	Piece Work	2. 7. 3.	(2.36)
Rollerman	Piece Work	3. 2. 10.	(3.14)
Doublers	Piece Work	2.10. 9.	(2.54)
Behinders	Piece Work	1. 6. 9.	(1.34)
Shearers	Piece Work	3. 1. 3.	(3.06)
Picklers	Piece Work	2. 4. 4.	(2.21)
Annealers	Piece Work	2. 1. 11.	(2.10)
Tinmen	Piece Work	2. 3. 6.	(2.17)
Assorters	Piece Work	2. 10. 5.	(2.52)
Boxers	Piece Work	2. 5. 1.	(2.25)
Mechanics	Time Rates	1. 18. 8.	(1.93)
General Labourers	Time Rates	1. 2. 9.	(1.14)

The earnings of female employees in the trade were disproportionately low, the average being 16 shillings and 9 pence (84p) per week for the Openers for what was extremely physically taxing work.

During the First World War increases in the cost of living depressed the purchasing power of employees' earnings, with those at the lower end of the incomes scale suffering especially. Attempts were made throughout the union movement to recover the situation; in the case of the tinplate trade this initiative achieved some success when an agreement was reached with the employers on the introduction of a supplement to the performance based rates of pay (piece rates), based on the cost of living index. However, this was no more than a temporary expedient, ceasing with the Armistice. Disappointingly, the prices of goods and services did not fall with the ending of hostilities as was expected and the unions successfully sought pay increases, obtaining the employers' agreement in 1919 to a 12½% advance on the standard rates and, in January 1920, to a 40% advance, increasing to 50% in April of the same year. The ease by which the increases had been secured by the unions reflected the unprecedented upswing in the demand for tinplate during this post-war period.

Prices charged by the manufacturers for their tinplate, too, surged forward at this time to peak at just under £3.00 per box in 1920. The unions considered that this was the right moment to pursue the introduction of a 'sliding scale' supplement to the basic rates which would rise or fall, as the case may be, relative to the price of tinplate. Unfortunately, before their proposition could be argued successfully, tinplate prices began to fall. Matters improved somewhat towards the end of the decade when an agreement was finally reached on a price related addition to tinplate workers earnings which became known throughout the trade as the 'sliding scale'. A further feature of the same agreement, effective from 1929, was the introduction of a 25% supplement to the 1874 rates.

The wages of production workers in the tinplate trade were made up of a number of elements viz. the datal rates (i.e. base rates) which often amounted to less than half of total wages, the bonus rates applied to performance, a cost of living bonus relating to movements in the Retail Prices Index and the Sliding Scale. In some cases non-process workers, too, were paid production bonuses, although the proportion of these to gross wages was smaller than those for production workers.

But the unions were concerned over not only the value of their

A group of people photographed (*c*. 1895) standing outside the entrance to the Cwmfelin Tinplate Works, Swansea. As most of the people in the group are women, some carrying children, it may be assumed that they are waiting on a Saturday for their husbands to finish work with their monthly pay.

members' labours to the employers but also with other factors which aggrieved members of the workforce. One they found particularly irritating was the length of time they had to wait between pay days. Up to 1907 many works maintained the practice of paying wages monthly in arrears with discretionary 'subs' (i.e. a proportion of the gross pay) being paid, if required by the employee, during the middle of the month. Soon after 1907 all employers paid wages fortnightly but continued pressure from the unions succeeded in bringing about the payment of wages on a weekly basis before the outbreak of the Great War.

Union activity also focused on the time and day of the pay out. In 1900, most works paid their employees at 4.00 p.m. on a Saturday. With the shortening of the working week wages could be collected at noon on the Saturday—a change welcomed not only by the workmen and their wives but also by the retailers of the tinplate towns who, consequently, were able to close their establishments earlier on Saturday evenings than hitherto. Later, the employers reluctantly agreed that workers should be able to receive their wages on Friday evenings. The hesitancy on the part of the employers to introduce this change stemmed from their concern for the safety of both employees and equipment; these might have been jeopardised as a consequence of the Friday evening pay out providing the opportunity for workers to purchase and consume excessive quantities of ale before turning up for work on the night shift. The unions, aware that a tinplate works was a particularly hazardous environment even for the most sober of men, supported and in some cases went as far as advocating stern disciplinary measures against anyone found to be at work whilst in a state of inebriation.

Although the intervals between the payment of wages had been reduced to one week, the period of contract for tinplate workers remained unchanged at one month. This, to the frustration of the workers, provided the employers with the opportunity to dismiss employees without notice at the end of each period of contract—a common feature when trading conditions slackened. However, even the customary month was often shortened by the employers for no justifiable reason and workers frequently found themselves dismissed with but a few hours notice. This practice had been challenged by the Steel Smelters Union as early as 1893 when the owners of the Morriston and Midland Tinplate Works stopped their mills and without notice laid off the Millmen. Civil action for damages for the men concerned was initiated by the Union but failed despite what was thought by many to have been an unanswerable case.

A similar situation arose in 1896 and again it involved tinplate workers in Morriston but this time those employed at the Upper Forest and Worcester Works. Mr. William Williams, the principal partner in the Company operating the Works, held the view that both the Upper Forest Works and the adjoining Worcester Works could not operate profitably in slack trading conditions. In order to maintain the Company's solvency he closed the two Works in March 1896, giving the employees no more than one week's notice.

Three of the active partners in the Company (Mrs. George Clarke, Mrs. Joseph Davies and Mrs. John Jones) were not altogether convinced of the efficacy of Williams's action and their dissension grew, along with the workers' hardships, throughout 1896. Angered by

Williams Williams of the Upper Forest and Worcester Works, Morriston.

their attitudes, publically proclaimed, Williams set about seeking to dissolve the partnership. Eventually, a compromise was reached with the three ladies agreeing to under-write any losses and by early March 1897 eight out of the ten mills at the Upper Forest Works had began rolling again. During their twelve months period of lock-out the workers had no income other than donations from others in the trade who were in employment. However, the amounts paid out were pitifully small e.g. on the 20th February 1897 a total of seventy eight pounds and ten shillings (£78.50) was distributed amongst 1500 employees and dependents at the rate of two shillings (10p) per adult and 6 pence (2½p) per child.[40]

What the Union viewed as unlawful frustration of its members' contracts was again litigiously tested, this time on behalf of the workmen at the Cilfrew Works at Neath. At Cilfrew in 1904, the employer had given the necessary one month's notice but had kept the men idle over the whole period and had not paid them any wages. Officials of the Steel Smelters were unbending in their opinion that, contractually, the men were either entitled to employment over the period of notice or, if that was not possible, to receive appropriate financial compensation. Since the Cilfrew case was just another example of what was a common practice within the trade, the Union expressed an intention of seeking a remedy even if it meant expensive litigation to test the case at the highest level of jurisdiction. The case was referred from the County Court to the Kings Bench Division of the High Court where it was heard before Mr. Justice Jelf in May 1904. Counsel for defendants, viz. Messrs. Rosser and Sons, the owners of the Works, submitted what they believed to be a strong case but it was the case presented by Counsel for the plaintiffs, supported by evidence given by the union and an employee (one Daniel Devonald) that secured the decision of Mr. Justice Jelf—a judgement confirmed by the Supreme Court after an appeal by the employers.

Over the eighty-five years of the Joint Conciliation Board's existence most of those who, in turn, were called upon to serve on it revealed a deep and abiding concern for both the future of the trade and the many who gained a living from it. Often the customary roles of masters and men were cast aside and replaced by unity of purpose for the good of the industry. After the initial recognition skirmishes that took place during the final quarter of the nineteenth century, the role of trades unions was accepted unequivocally by the masters. But in those early days when the union movement was desperately seeking to establish itself and the participants in union activities found themselves to be the targets of their masters acrimony, a few turned their backs on Wales and sought employment in the emerging American tinplate industry. On 4th July 1874 Evan Davies, then a recent emigrant to Pittsburgh, wrote to his former colleagues in Wales revealing at the beginning of his letter his reason for departing from his homeland:

> Leaving of the land of our fathers because of our connection with the Tinplate Workers Union is well known to our countrymen. Because of this Union, we were on strike in the Cwmbwrla tin works for six months and as others who did not belong to the Union came in our place, some of us decided to go to America and the Union paid our passage.[41]

Ironically, the vision of America as the land of opportunity for trade union activists was quickly dispelled when, after having crossed the Atlantic in search of employment, they discovered that ex-patriate

Welshmen, fully aware of the problems associated with organised labour, had taken up managerial positions in the American industry. Many were to become key men in the American steel and tinplate industry: F.R. Phillips formed the Welsh-American Tinplate Company with a capital of over one million dollars and in 1905 John Charles Williams master-minded the formation of the Phillips Sheet and Tinplate Company, later re-named the Wierton Steel Company. Williams became a millionaire and remained at the helm of his firm until his death in 1936.[42] These Welsh-American masters were even more determined than their Welsh colleagues to resist the threat of unionisation—a stance clearly confirmed in an 1880 letter from David Davies, a Welsh exile and trade unionist in Pittsburgh.

My intention is to tell my compatriots that America is not a paradise. Many, like myself when I was in Wales, think that this country is a wonderful Canaan and that one only has to cross the ocean to obtain confort and happiness. It is also said that America is a free country. Yes, it is so free that, as an Englishman said, if you have no boots you can go barefooted and so it is exactly. I remember the old saying that every mountain is white until it is seen and that was America to me and thousands besides. It is true that some are doing well in this country and others fairly well but there are thousands who are sorry that they ever thought of coming to America. Yes, there are thousands of men to be seen out of work in Pittsburgh and if only they had the means, many would have gone back to the Old Country with those who returned last winter. I do not doubt that I and many of my fellows would have been among them.

I am sorry to say that we are still on strike. It is likely that we will be so for some time if we do not get work somewhere else. Each one of us is doing his best to get it, but many up to now have failed. This is not surprising as the country is in such disorder. We are determined to stand up for our rights until the end if we can keep body and soul together. The works have not been going since the strike began despite the efforts of some of the masters to get men in our places. Two or three offered to blacksheep us but we sent to them and they promised to keep away and give us fair play.

I heard from friends in Maesteg that there is a movement on foot to make a collection which will be sent over to help us. It is true, fellow workmen, that we are in need of help because many families here have seen hard times and some who have been in the country only nine to twelve months. So if you feel it in your hearts to do this we shall be very grateful. We heard about the Union in Wales and intended paying into it if that had been acceptable but within twelve days we were on strike.[43]

Similar sentiments were expressed by a T. Puntan of Newport, Kentucky when he wrote on the 7th November 1881, to Robert Roberts of Ebbw Vale.

I am sorry to say that I and Oakley, my son-in-law, have not had work of any kind since last June because of the general strike in the Cincinnati region. The reason for the present strike is as follows. It has always been the custom for the masters at the mills at Cincinnati, Covington, Newport, Aurora, Terre Haute, Zanesville, and Portsmouth to pay their workmen in each branch, especially those into the chief branches, ten per cent more than the masters of the mills in Pittsburgh pay their workmen because it is hotter here in the South and the material is not the same as in Pittsburgh.

It seems that the chief purpose of the masters is to break the union among the workmen here as did the masters of the Welsh works years ago. There is the same tyrannical, oppressive, and overbearing spirit in the masters on this side of the Atlantic as on the other. At the beginning of the strike they gave warning that only non union men would in future be employed by them.

These non unionists are called black sheep and the unionists are called white sheep. Agents are sent to recruit black sheep from various parts of this country and even from Europe, Wales and England. I saw an account of about twenty-three who had come from some part of Wales under the flattering influence of a man called John Price but I am glad to say that these Welshman, when they understood that they had been misled, behaved worthy of the courage of the Welsh nation, opposing this traitor and his fellow traitors. They refused to work, joined the union, and went to earn their living in places where there was no enmity between labour and capital.[44]

Evidently, the hostile opposition of the American masters to trade unionism continued unrelentingly until the outbreak of the First World

War, revealing itself when officials of the unions representing Welsh tinplate workers visited the USA to obtain, at first hand, knowledge of the procedures and practices employed by the Americans. In the report of his 1913 visit Sidney Jones of the Steel Smelters Union referred to the difficulties he had experienced in gaining access to the Shenango Works at Newcastle, Pennsylvania (where, incidentally, the tinhouse superintendent was reported to be a man born and bred in Pontardawe). Jones wrote in his report: 'When I got to the office, the manager, after shaking hands and exchanging greetings, told me that under ordinary circumstances he did not allow anyone to go into the works without a permit from Mr. Davies of the Steel Trust (Mr. S.A. Davies, Vice-President of the United States Steel Trust), but in my case he had received a message over the 'phone informing him I was coming, and upon no consideration was I to go into the works'. Again, when seeking permission to enter the Jones and Laughlin's plant at Woodlawn, Pittsburgh, Sidney Jones met with similar resistance.[45]

Ivor Gwynne, President of the Tin and Sheet Millmen's Association, also visited America in the same year as Sidney Jones and in his subsequent report commented on the struggle of the Amalgamated Iron, Steel and Tinplate Workers Association to gain recognition in the tinplate works at Steubenville, Ohio. Gwynne reported that he 'had the honour of sharing the platform with a Mr. Davies (the Assistant Secretary) and a Mr. Griffiths (the Organiser) of the America Association' in addressing the workers seeking recognition, many of whom, like their officials, were emigrant Welshmen and who had stood firm in their belief despite several months of enforced idleness.[46] Eventually, the American unions succeeded in gaining recognition from their employers, possibly influenced by the success of the Welsh Industry's Joint Conciliation Board in proving that, under the right conditions, the opposing interests of employers and trade unions need not inhibit effective management.

Tributes paid to the work of the Joint Conciliation Board confirm its effectiveness. Sir Ernest Lever, when Chairman of The Steel Company of Wales, said of the Board: 'It is no exaggeration to say that in no industry in any part of the country has there been achieved that high degree of co-operation between management and men that exists in this Joint Industrial Council. To me it typifies the spirit of collaboration which is wanted in this world today, more than it ever was wanted before'. Responding on behalf of the Workmen Mr. (later Sir) Harry

Douglass, Assistant General Secretary of the Iron and Steel Trades Confederation, stated: 'I would say that if any lesson taught me and encourages me to hope for the future, it was the experience of the Tinplate Council. If any industry can get a relationship between the employed and the employers such as has been sustained here for more than half a century, then there is hope for that particular industry'.[47]

These were fitting testimonies to a unique partnership.

NOTES

[1] Minchinton, W., op. cit.

[2] Ibid.

[3] Brooke, E.H., op. cit.; Wainwright, D., *Men of Steel: The History of Richard Thomas and his Family*. (Quiller Press, London, 1896).

[4] Warren, Kenneth, op. cit.

[5] Hancocks, H., *History of Tinplate Manufacture in Llanelli* (Unpublished MA thesis, University College, Swansea, 1965); Davies, J.H., op. cit.; Jenkins, Rhys, op. cit.

[6] Davies, J.H., op. cit.

[7] *The Cambrian,* 24th July 1906.

[8] Chappell, E.H., *Historic Melingriffith* (Cardiff, 1940).

[9] Report of the Commissioners on the Employment of Children in Factories, 1833.

[10] Report of the Royal Commissioners on Education in Wales, 1847.

[11] Wynne-Evans, L., *Education in Industrial Wales, 1700-1900* (Avalon Books, Cardiff, 1976).

[12] Thomas, P.S., Pamphlet No.4 'Industrial Relations' in Williams, D. Trefor (Ed.) *The Economic Development of Swansea District to 1921* (Cardiff, 1940).

[13] *The Mariner* Vol. XIII, No. 2, 30th November, 1895; *Who Was Who,* Vol. I, 1897-1915 (A & C Black, London, 1920).

[14] Collis, E.L. and Hilditch, J., *Report on the Conditions of Employment in the Manufacture of Tinplates* (Comd. 6394 (1912).

[15] Wynne-Evans, L. op. cit.

[16] Minutes of a Meeting of the Workmen's Side of the Tinplate Trades Joint Industrial Council, 17th July 1936.

[17] Wilkins, C., *History of the Iron, Steel and Tinplate Trades* (Merthyr Tydfil, 1903).

[18] Minchton, W., op. cit.

[19] Player Mss.

[20] Documents in Author's Collection.

[21] Pugh, Sir Arthur, *Men of Steel* (Iron and Steel Trades Confederation, 1951).

[22] Kennerley, E.J., 'Caerleon Mills and Ponthir Tinplate Works', *Gwent Local History,* No. 49, Autumn 1980.

[23] *Report of the Commission Appointed into the Truck System 1871,* Minchinton, W., Ibid.

[24] Thomas, P.S., op. cit.; Pugh, Sir Arthur, op. cit.

[25] Thomas, P.S., op. cit. ·

[26] Chappell, E.H., op. cit.

[27] Jones, E.H., *A Study of Industrial Relations in the British Tinplate Industry 1874-1939* (Unpublished M.A. thesis, University of Wales, 1940).

[28] Thomas, P.S., op. cit.

[29] Pugh, Sir Arthur, op. cit.

[30] Thomas, P.S., op. cit.

[31] *The Cambrian,* 1st May 1874.

[32] Pugh, Sir Arthur, op. cit.

[33] Pugh, Sir Arthur, op. cit.; Minchinton, W., op. cit

[34] Ibid.

[35] Ibid.

[36] Leng, Philip J., *The Welsh Dockers* (G.W. & A. Hesketh, Ormskirk, 1981); Pugh, Sir Arthur, ibid.

[37] British Steel plc., Records.

[38] Pugh, Sir Arthur, op. cit.

[39] Ibid.

[40] *The Industrial World* (22nd February and 5th March 1897).

[41] Conway, A. (Ed)., *The Welsh in America: Letters from the Immigrants* (University of Wales Press, Cardiff, 1961).

[42] Hartman, E.G., *Americans from Wales* (The Christopher Publishing House, Boston, 1967).

[43] Conway, A. (Ed)., op. cit.

[44] Ibid.

[45] Jones, S., *Report to British Steel Smelters, Mill, Iron, Tinplate and Kindred Trades Association on Visit to America* (November 1913).

[46] Gwynne, I.H., *My Impressions of the American Tinplate Trade* (Report to Tin and Sheet Millmen's Association, 1913).

[47] Addresses given to a meeting of the Tinplate Trades Joint Conciliation Board on 29th November 1957 (British Steel plc Records).

6. THE END OF AN ERA

Perhaps if we could picture the days of long ago,
When all the power they had to use was got from water flow,
When sturdy man was forced to slave for sixteen hours or more,
And ev'ry circumstance increased the hardship ofthe poor,
When women tended furnaces and boys were made to work
At heavy tasks that adult men might reasonably shirk;
When rain and wind could penetrate the broken roofs and doors
With drainage non-existent on the sunk uneven floors:
With ample vindication should we find ourselves aghast
To contemplate the conditions of the worker of the past.
And feel devoutly thankful that in these enlightened days.
His surroundings have been bettered in a thousand simple ways.

Extract from the 'Lament for Morfa Mawr' by Charles Fern (1946).

The evolution of discrete communities within the South Wales towns of Llanelli, Pontardulais, Gorseinon, Morriston, Pontardawe, Briton Ferry, Port Talbot, Ebbw Vale and Pontypool is directly correlated to the growth of the tinplate industry. Thankfully, the tinplate towns and their communities have survived the cataclysm, in the form of the modern, high capacity plants, that destroyed their nuclei, the hand mill works. Only Llanelli (Trostre Works) and Ebbw Vale (Ebbw Vale Works) nowadays have any direct association with the manufacture of tinplate. Unlike their predecessors, the 1950's vintage cold reduction and electrolytic tinning plants of Trostre and Velindre were largely socially isolated, mere islands of employment in which the workpeople were drawn from a much wider catchment area than that of the distinctly parochial hand mills. By comparison with the latter, little affinity exists between the contemporary works and their neighbouring communities.

The death knell of the hand mill plants sounded in 1924 when the series of rolls within the Ashland, Kentucky, Continuous Mill turned for the first time to produce steel in strip form. The transplant of the American-developed technology into the UK industry at Ebbw Vale in 1938 hastened the demise, the end finally arriving in the nineteen-sixties following a comprehensive re-structuring of the industry undertaken under the aegis of the Steel Company of Wales Ltd. Before

1938, the closure of any of the total of 83 hand mill plants that at one stage or another had been in operation in South Wales/West Gloucestershire was specifically related to market and/or financial conditions.

The Ebbw Vale project changed all that. Its creator, William Firth, then Chairman of Richard Thomas & Co., was regarded with some disdain by his fellow tinplate makers who viewed what in concept was a far-sighted proposal for the future of the British tinplate industry, as nothing more than a vehicle for his egoism. His background—he had entered the industry via the London-based merchanting firm he had founded at the age of 21—and his aggressive determination to oversee the industry's rationalisation did nothing to endear him to the patrimonial owners and so he failed to secure their acquiescence to his proposals. Undaunted, he relentlessly pursued the manifestation of his dream of importing continuous strip mill technology from America to Ebbw Vale. Physically constrained within a narrow valley some thirty miles from the nearest port, the Ebbw Vale site was logistically unsuitable for an integrated plant of the modern era. Many of the new American strip mill plants had been built in locations that offered optimum facilities in terms of plant layout, transportation of raw materials and finished goods and future expansion. Furthermore, with the actual cost of the Ebbw Vale scheme (in the region of £10m. to £11m.) being more than double the original estimate of £4.5m., the financial burden imposed on Richard Thomas & Co. by Firth in the pursuit of his dream forced the Company to seek assistance from the Bank of England. An enquiry into the firm's affairs was seen as a necessary pre-requisite to the provision of assistance by the Bank. Featuring prominently among the recommendations of the Enquiry Committee was the call for greater co-operation within the trade on matters such as the distribution of orders, the withdrawal from service of outdated plant and, significantly, the establishment of a Control Committee, comprising experienced and interested parties, to monitor the affairs of the Company.[1]

Amongst the influential people nominated to serve on the Control Committee were Sir Charles Wright, Chairman of Guest Keen & Baldwins Limited—a company also engaged in the manufacture of steel and tinplate—and E.H. Lever of the Prudential Insurance Company, the nominee of the shareholders of Richard Thomas & Co. The amiable relationship that developed between Sir Charles and

Ernest Lever whilst serving as members of the Committee later was to bear fruit in other directions. Soon, both were involved in planning the future course of the entire industry, and in doing so resurrected Baldwin's concept of building a second strip mill in South Wales, only this time at a location nearer to the coast and to the tinplate industry's hitherto traditional base in West Wales than the Ebbw Vale mill.[2]

Undoubtedly, the intervention of the Second World War saved Ebbw Vale from becoming a financial disaster. Had it not been for wartime demands for strip mill products the burdensome interest charges on the capital borrowed to finance the reconstruction of the works might well have led to the Company's insolvency. As it was, the upwards trend in output from the mill continued throughout the war and ironically many of the old type tinplate works in East Wales benefitting from the excess rolling capacity of the Ebbw Vale Mill when its product—good quality continuously rolled sheet—came onto the market and was used in the tinning departments of the older works.

Their rejection of Firth's attempts to obtain a concerted and rational approach to the modernisation issue typified the self-interest, self-preservation attitude that prevailed amongst the majority of tinplate manufacturers. Similarly, measures designed to introduce a degree of rationality into the apportionment of business during times when the market was weak failed because of the stronger desire of the manufacturers to maintain their independence and individuality. A quota system, agreed by them and introduced in 1925, was soon abandoned after having been breached by several of the original participants when trading conditions improved. For the workforce, periods of trade recession naturally brought anxiety over job security. However, from 1933 onwards, the fearful consequences for the workforce of a serious fall in the demand for tinplate were largely ameliorated by the gradual introduction of the six-hour shift system within the trade, for which a further full mill crew of six men (viz. Rollerman, Doubler, Furnaceman, Behinder and First and Second Helpers) was required.

Notwithstanding these measures, unemployment rose sharply in parallel with the 1938 recession. However, this down-turn was short-lived as the acceleration of the armed forces re-equiping programme brought about a recovery in activity throughout 1939. Even allowing for the fact that the output of the Ebbw Vale Strip Mill equated to the combined production of fifty hand mills, very few of the old-type

220

works were idle at the mid-point of the year by which time the preparation for war was beginning to gain momentum. Young men employed in the trade were drafted into the forces and works such as the Amman, the Raven and the Glynbeudy that had been idle for some time were requisitioned for the storage of war materials. The Llangennech Tinplate Works, too, was taken over by the Admiralty for use as a storage depot—a function it has continued to perform until recently. Other establishments converted to ordnance work and storage were the Western, Ashburnham, Old Lodge, Old Castle (partly) and Kidwelly Works in the Llanelli area. The partially-closed Melingriffith Works at Cardiff was converted to manufacture armaments and many of the former tinplaters, especially the craftsmen , were to prove their worth in the highly skilled machining and assembly tasks undertaken at the establishment during the war.[3]

Attempts at the sequestration of an operating tinplate works for war work sometimes met with stern resistance from the work-people who, unlike the owning companies that gained compensation for their losses under the tinplate pooling scheme, received no such financial inducement. At Pontypool, for example, the Ministry of Supply sought to requisition the Central Works for the purpose of storing materials produced at the Glascoed Ordnance Factory. The proposal received Board of Trade support with the proviso that the displaced labour be redeployed to the Avondale Works, some four miles away, and the Abertillery Works, a distance of thirteen miles from Pontypool. Despite overtures to the Board of Trade by their union and the local Member of Parliament, the workmen's protests fell on deaf ears; the war was intensifying and the social inconvenience of a small group of workers at Pontypool was a mere triviality in comparison with more pressing needs. The requisitioning of Pontypool's Central Works, along with twenty-five others, consequently proceeded to plan.

The movement of labour away from the trade in the first four years of the War took place on an unprecedented scale (see Appendix 'C' for the manning structure of the industry in 1939 and 1941). By September 1941, it was estimated that 12,000 workers had left the industry. Faced with severe manning problems, during the last part of 1941 the Workmen's Side of the Joint Industrial Council agreed to the abandonment of the six-hour shift system and the re-introduction of the less labour-demanding eight-hour shifts. In the same year, the Essendon Committee—a Committee under the Chairmanship of Lord

221

Essendon and comprising three employers viz. Capt. Leighton Davies of Baldwins, J.E. James (Richard Thomas & Co.) and Llewellyn David of the Taibach Tinplate Works together with three union representatives—P. Owen of the T. & G.W.U., R.G. Lewis, N.U.G.M.W. and John Brown, BISAKTA—was formed to investigate and report on the feasibility of concentrating production in a few modern, highly productive, cost effective units.

The following table, depicting the pre-war distribution of the industry's productive capacity throughout eighty small works with outputs ranging from 1600 to 17000 basis boxes per week, clearly demonstrates both the archaic state of the industry at that time and the problems faced by the members of Lord Essendon's Committee.

PRE-WORLD WAR II DISTRIBUTION OF PRODUCTIVE CAPACITY WITHIN TINPLATE TRADE

(Source: Documents in Author's Collection)

Name of Owner and Works	NO. OF MILLS AND CAPACITY	
	No. of Mills	Capacity per Week in Basis Boxes (20 Basis Boxes = 1 Imperial Ton) (Approx.)
Richard Thomas and Baldwins Ltd.		
1. Aber	8	8,000
2. Abercarn	12	12,900
3. Aberdulais	6	6,300
4. Alyn	4	3,100
5. Bryn	3	3,800
6. Burry	16	16,680
7. Cardonnel	4	4,200
8. Cwmbwrla	8	7,300
9. Cwmfelin	15	15,900
10. Cynon	3	2,385
11. Edlogan	3	2,670
12. Ely	2	2,220
13. Lydney	11	11,400
14. Melingriffith	12	12,000

| Name of Owner and Works | NO. OF MILLS AND CAPACITY | |
	No. of Mills	Capacity per Week in Basis Boxes (20 Basis Boxes = 1 Imperial Ton) (Approx.)
Richard Thomas and Baldwins Ltd.		
(*cont.*)		
15. Morfa	5	5,575
16. Pencoed	3	3,000
17. R. T. Mills	8	11,250
18. South Wales	10	10,150
19. Treforest	4	3,200
20. Ebbw Vale	50	60,000
21. Byass	12	14,000
22. Gowerton	2	1,700
23. King's Dock	14	16,200
24. Wern	4	3,900
Grovesend Steel & Tinplate Co. Ltd.		
25. Amman	3	3,200
26. Cambria	3	3,290
27. Dyffryn	15	15,500
28. Dynevor	3	2,700
29. Gorseinon	9	11,550
30. Grovesend	9	10,125
31. Hendy	4	4,600
32. Mardy	6	7,150
W. Gilbertson & Co. Ltd.		
33. Pontardawe	6	7,100
34. Glanrhyd	6	6,300
35. Glynbeudy	4	3,200
36. Clayton Tinplate Co. Ltd.	7	7,600
	294	320,145

Name of Owner and Works	NO. OF MILLS AND CAPACITY	
	No. of Mills	Capacity per Week in Basis Boxes (20 Basis Boxes = 1 Imperial Ton) (Approx.)
The Briton Ferry Steel Co. Ltd. **Briton Ferry, Neath, Glam** *(cont.)* 37. Aberavon		
38. Ferry	4	4,000
39. Ffrwdwyllt	4	4,150
40. Gwalia	5	5,200
41. Melyn	4	4,250
42. Morriston	6	6,200
43. Resolven	11	11,000
44. Villers	4	3,950
45. Vivian	7	7,7175
	3	3,600
	48	49,525
Llanelly Associated Tinplate Co.Ltd.		
46. Ashburnham	4	4,250
47. Kidwelly	7	6,850
48. Old Castle	14	16,720
49. Old Lodge	6	5,800
50. Teilo	6	6,750
51. Western	8	8,000
	45	48,370
Partridge, Jones & John Paton Ltd. **Pontypool, Mon.**		
52. Caerlon	3	2,750
53. Central	4	5,400
54. Osbourne	2	1,600
55. Pontymister	4	3,900
56. Pontypool	4	4,050
57. Waterloo	4	4,300
	21	22,000

	NO. OF MILLS AND CAPACITY	
Name of Owner and Works	No. of Mills	Capacity per Week in Basis Boxes (20 Basis Boxes = 1 Imperial Ton) (Approx.)
Bynea (Subsidiaries of Bynea Steel Works Ltd. 58. Webb, Shakespeare & Williams Ltd., Pontardulais	4	4,000
59. St. David's Tinplate Co. (1927) Ltd., Loughor	10	11,100
	14	15,100
Upper Forest & Worcester Steel and Tinplate Works Ltd., Morriston, Swansea 60. Upper Forest	16	16,800
INDEPENDENTS 61. Abertillery Works Ltd., Abertillery, Mon.	7	7,150
62. Anglo-Welsh Tinplate Co. Ltd. Ystradgynlais, Nr. Swansea	3	2,700
63. Avondale Tinplate Co. Ltd. Pontnewydd, Mon.	6	8,250
64. Baglan Bay Tinplate Co. Ltd. Briton Ferry, Neath, West Glam.	8	9,550
65. Beaufort Works Ltd., Morriston Swansea	9	8,700
66. Copper Miners Tinplate Co. Ltd. Cwmavon, Port Talbot	8	7,600
67. D. R. David & Son Ltd., Port Talbot	4	4,500
68. Dulais Tinplate Co. Ltd. Pontardulais	4	4,650
69. Elba Tinplate Co. Ltd., Crymlyn, Burrows, Swansea	12	17,000

| Name of Owner and Works | NO. OF MILLS AND CAPACITY | |
	No. of Mills	Capacity per Week in Basis Boxes (20 Basis Boxes = 1 Imperial Ton) (Approx.)
INDEPENDENTS *(cont.)*		
70. Eaglesbush Tinplate Works Ltd. Neath	7	9,000
71. Fairwood Tinplate Co. Ltd., Gowerton	4	4,150
72. Glynhir Tinplate Co. Ltd., Pontardulais	3	3,500
73. Gyrnos Tinplate Co. (1921) Ltd., Lower Cwmtwrch, Swansea	4	4,000
74. Morlais Tinplate Co. Ltd., Llangennech	4	3,950
75. Park Tinplate Co. Ltd., Clydach, Nr Swansea	2	1,800
76. Pemberton Tinplate Co. Ltd., Llanelly	4	4,400
77. Phoenix Tinplate Co. Ltd., Cwmtwrch, Nr Swansea	3	2,950
78. John Player & Sons Ltd., Clydach, Nr Swansea	4	4,520
79. Redbrook Tinplate Co. Ltd., Pontnewydd Mon:—		
Redbrook	4	4,350
Tynewydd	3	3,650
80. Ystalyfera Tinplate Co. Ltd., Ystalyfera, Nr Swansea	4	4,400
	107	120,770

After considerable debate, a proposal to permanently reduce capacity within the trade by some 30% and based on the Essendon Committee's recommendations was finally adopted by the Tinplate Conference at a meeting of members on 25th May 1945 and shortly afterwards received the ratification of the President of the Board of

Trade. In effect, the rationalisation programme, known as the Tinplate Redundancy Scheme, enabled capacity to be reduced by 30% i.e. from 30 million boxes of tinplate per annum to 21 million boxes per annum; this roughly equated to the sterilisation of 165 out of the 545 hand mills then available within the trade. The six larger groups of Richard Thomas and Baldwins Ltd., (the amalgamation of the two principal concerns in the trade took place in January 1945), the Briton Ferry Steel Company Ltd., the Llanelli Associated Tinplate Companies Ltd., Partridge, Jones and John Paton Ltd., Bynea Steel Works Ltd., and the Upper Forest and Worcester Steel & Tinplate Works Ltd. agreed to reduce the capacities of their plants by 25% without compensation. Thus, financial assistance was to be paid for the permanent sterilisation of only 5% of the six 'groups' productive capacity but the full 30% in the case of the twenty independent producers. The scale of the compensation was agreed at £5,500 for each mill of average capacity (1,073 boxes per week) taken out of commission either by one of the 'groups' or by one of the 'independents' remaining in the trade, and £7,500 per mill for the 'independents' undertaking to withdraw completely from tinplate manufacture.[4] It was proposed that of the eighty works covered by the scheme, twenty-nine would remain closed following the restoration of peace. A few, such as the Abercarn works in North Gwent, were to be re-opened to tin the blackplate rolled in other establishments, particularly Ebbw Vale (see Appendix 'A' for full list of works and key dates).

With the tinplate owners receiving compensation for reducing capacities under the Tinplate Redundancy Scheme, a comparable arrangement was devised for the work-force despite the acute shortage of labour that developed after the ending of hostilities. At a meeting of the Employers' Association on 2nd September 1946 it was agreed that all members (i.e. the employers) would contribute one penny (½p) per box towards the establishment of a fund—the Tinplate Trade Labour fund—to financially compensate employees displaced as a consequence of the envisaged development of the new strip mill and cold reduction plants in West Wales. But with demand gaining momentum in 1945 and manning within the trade standing at no more than 11,000 (compared with 23,000 in 1939) the recruitment, not displacement, of labour had to be given emphasis.[5]

By 1949, successful efforts to induce workers back into the trade had brought the number employed up to around 14,000, but more were

227

needed. Little success had been achieved by the employment of European Voluntary Workers (Czechs, Poles, Slavs etc.) or indeed with labour obtained from Northern Ireland as at least 1,000 out of the 1,400 engaged from these sources quickly drifted away, possibly finding the work too onerous. In an attempt to halt the decline, the Joint Industrial Council for the trade made several approaches to the Government to secure the release of cold rolls operatives, bundlers and junior mill grades from National Services but all failed, the last approach, made in 1950, being thwarted by the outbreak of the Korean War. Consideration had to be given to obtaining labour from other sources. A possible solution offered by the Ministry of Labour—the employment of suitable labour from amongst the unemployed in Italy—was examined in detail and finally accepted by both sides of the industry.

Recruitment missions were quickly established and interview sessions arranged in Naples and Genoa. By the end of 1950, 317 Italians had entered the trade, the number increasing to 857 by the close of 1952. Housed in a hostel at Morriston, their assimilation into the industrial and social communities of South Wales naturally presented problems but by the time of the termination of the recruitment missions in 1956 the exercise that had brought 2,259 Italians into the trade was acknowledged by all to be an unqualified success. Many acquired the skills involved in tinplate manufacture in a surprisingly short time, moving up into senior positions such as Rollerman, Furnacemen, Doublers etc. Some even settled permanently in Wales, securing employment in the cold reduction plants at Trostre and Velindre or, after having left the tinplate trade, in other industries. Those who expressed a wish to return to Italy when faced with redundancy at the time of the closure of the hand-mill were given a free passage home.[6]

The coming on stream of the Trostre (1951) and the Velindre (1956) cold reduction plants was another milestone for the industry and one which signalled the demise of the old hand-mill plants. The prelude to a comprehensive re-organisation of tinplate manufacturing in South Wales was the 1945 amalgamation of Richard Thomas and Company Ltd. and Baldwins Ltd. But this unification of interests, steered through by Ernest Lever of Richard Thomas & Co. and Sir Charles Wright of Baldwins, did not stop at that point. Further discussions between Richard Thomas and Baldwins Ltd. and other tinplate

228

The American Tin Plate Works—the first in the U.S.A., c. 1873.

229

Trademark of the 'American Tin Plate Company', Elwood, Indiana, 1891. It symbolises the replacement of the Welsh product (the lion) by American tin plate (the eagle).

manufacturers in South Wales viz. Guest Keen Baldwins, John Lysaght of Newport and the Llanelli Associated Tinplate Companies Ltd. bore fruit in the form of The Steel Company of Wales Ltd., incorporated on the 1st May 1947, with Lever as its first Chairman. The new Company took control of eighteen old style works—fifteen of which were still in operation i.e. the Asburnham, Burry, Dyffryn, Glanrhyd, Gorseinon, Grovesend, King's Dock, Lydney, Mardy, Melingriffith, Old Castle, Pontardawe, R.T. Mills, Teilo and Western. The three idle works taken over were the Hendy at Pontardulais and the Morfa and South Wales Works, both of which were situated in Llanelli.

With the new cold reduction plants making an impact in terms of the scale of output and the lower cost of the product, the final chapter of the story of the old-style works was drawing to a close. On the 31st January 1953, the Asburnham, Dyffryn, Glanrhyd, Grovesend and Western Works of the Steel Company of Wales Ltd. the Elba Works. Swansea and the Ffrwdwyllt, Villiers and Vivian Works of the Briton Ferry Group all ceased to manufacture tinplate. By May, production had also been brought to a halt at the R.T. Mills, the Gwalia and the Upper Forest and Worcester Works. The Byass Works of R.T. & B. suffered a similar fate in April 1954, and four years later, The Steel Company of Wales Ltd. finally closed all its then existing hand mill plants viz. Kings Dock, Old Castle, Lydney, Melingriffith, Teilo and Mardy, and R.T. & B. its Clayton Works.

The last works to close in terms of the simultaneous cessation of mill and tinhouse production was that at Redbrook (Gwent) in 1961. A few of the old style Works—Elba, R.T. Mills, Burry, Dyffryn and Abercarn Works—continued to operate as satellites to the modern cold reduction plants for the performance of specific functions such as secondary processing, packaging materials manufacture and storage. Hot dip tinning was practised at the Elba and Abercarn Works for a while longer but, apart from the R.T. Mills Works in Llanelli, all were gradually disposed of throughout the nineteen seventies and early eighties by the British Steel Corporation which had acquired the assets of the Steel Company of Wales Limited and Richard Thomas & Baldwins Limited when the iron and steel industry was nationalised in 1967.[7]

The reduction in the numbers employed in the trade over the period 1947 to 1957 is outlined in Appendix 'D'. Employees who had been unable to obtain employment in the cold reduction plants and who, therefore, were forced to seek work outside of the industry, received financial compensation under the Tinplate Trades Labour Fund. Payments of up to a maximum of £350, based on an employee's average earnings and length of service, were made out of the fund which over the years of its existence accumulated a total of £874,000 from the contributions made by the employers. A similar fund was set up for staff employees, into which the employers again contributed a total of £204,000. Payments made out the funds totalled £642,000 for the process, craft and services workers and £141,000 for staff grades. Both funds preceeded by many years the State Redundancy Payments Scheme which, upon its introduction in 1965, brought their useful purpose to an end. Monies remaining in the funds at the time of their winding up were donated to educational establishments throughout South Wales.[8]

With the closure of the hand-mill works, an epoch in the industrial and social development of South Wales came to an end. Works in which blood, sweat and tears could not extinguish the flame of desire

231

within the work-people to overcome their adversity and create a close, supportive community, were no more. All the familiar sounds of the old tinplate works—the whirr of the rolls, the hiss of steam, the crash of metal against metal, the cries of anguish, the laughter and the songs of the workers—became silent. The affinity that built-up between the workers in, collectively, easing the burden of work was carried through into the wider community of village and town. All but a few aspects have disappeared. Sporting activities (rugby, soccer and cricket) and music, especially, played an important social role in the tinplate communities. Charles Wilkins reflected on the fact that 'one of Madam Patti's chosen tenors' was a workman employed at a Morriston tinplate works.[9] The Morriston Orpheus, the Manselton (Swansea), Pontardulais and Llanelli male choirs of international repute have had, and in some cases still have, within their ranks members who at some time or other worked within the trade.

The social structure that emerged within the hand-mill plants has long since disappeared. At its head was the manager, whose authoritarian discipline was feared by all. Rollerman were said to have been reduced to tears at the thought of having to appear before the manager, especially if the reason for their appearance was the breakage of a roll in the mill—an event that, even if not their fault, usually meant a period of suspension from work for the man concerned. Next in the hierarchy came the foreman or 'gaffer', but it was the Rollermen who had conferred upon them an exalted status within the community. Their awareness of their status limited the extent to which they conversed with the Behinders, the junior man in the crew, to but a few essential instructions. In their social habits, the Rollerman mixed with their own kind; in the pubs and clubs they gathered together to discuss their craft. As one commentator aptly observed of the conversations within the hostelries of the tinplate districts: 'More tinplate was made in these establishments than in any works'.

In time, the physical impact of the old-style works on the landscape of South Wales will also disappear. Already communities in which tinplate manufacture was formerly carried out have accepted and adjusted to new industries and, hopefully, the tradition of the skilful, honest endeavour of the Welsh worker will continue to be recognised internationally.

A measure of satisfaction mixed with pride must be gained from the fact that the tinplate industries of, amongst other countries, the U.S.A. and, surprisingly, Russia, were founded on the knowledge and skills of the Welsh tinplaters. Those who sought new opportunities across the Atlantic became the backbone of the American tinplate industry. One estimate put the number of tinplate workers emigrating to the U.S.A. from West Wales in the post-McKinley Tariff period at 'not fewer than 6000'. They settled principally in the tinplate producing areas of Philadelphia and Newcastle, Pennsylvania, in Wheeling and Wierton, West Virginia, Ferry and Steubenville, Ohio and in Gas City, Indiana.[10] American politicians, eager to protect their emerging industry, sought to break the monopoly of the Welsh Manufacturers. McKinley succeeded with his tariff proposals only after hard and ruthless campaigning, during which one of his strongest supporters, the brilliant and politically powerful Senator Aldrich, gave the following testimony to the skill of the Welsh tinplaters:

It is claimed that the Welsh people have such a peculiar aptitude for, or knowledge of, this manufacture as to make successful production elsewhere impossible. The imposition of this duty will transfer the industry from Wales to the United States . . .[11]

In 1873, one of the many who left these shores for America wrote to his former colleagues in Wales and in his letter confirmed the influence of the Welsh in the American tinplate trade during its early days. The letter began thus:

Undoubtedly you have heard that a tinplate works has been opened in America and that another one is being built. The first, the American Tinplate Works stands on the banks of the Ohio about fifty miles from Pittsburgh by a small country town called Wellsville whose inhabitants number about three thousand. Most of the owners are thorough Welshmen, born in Glamorganshire. The other, that is the United States Tinplate Works, is on the banks of the Monongahela River about fifteen miles from Pittsburgh. The overseer of this works will also be a Welshman . . .[12]

The first tinplate works in Russia, the Moscow Metal Works, was built around 1911 to the design of a Welshman, S.R. Cound, who gained his knowledge and experience of the tinplate trade at the Gorseinon works. (Some time after his return from Moscow, presumably before the 1917 Revolution, he was appointed the first manager of the prestigious Elba Works, Swansea). He took with him to Russia many Welshmen and their families to fill key positions within the works. Tom Griffiths of the Steel Smelters Union visited the Moscow Metal Works in 1913 and his subsequent report is a fascinating account of not only how the Welsh acquitted themselves in a completely foreign environment but also of the social conditions endured by the working class of Moscow. His report, reproduced in full in Appendix 'E', says of the Moscow Welsh:

> The Welshmen have got into the Russian method of living—up early in the morning to work and down late at night in all the places of amusement that are provided for the people. They earn good money, and some of them are saving for the rainy day; yet the men and their wives take part in all the sports and pastimes, such as football, tennis, hockey etc.[13]

It is pleasing to note that even in this modern era of cold reduction and electrolytic tinning, the expertise of the Welsh in tinplate making has been duly recognised by Russia. In the early nineteen-seventies, when new tinplate manufacturing equipment of British design was under construction at Magnitogorsk, Siberia, several Welshmen from the Trostre and Velindre Works were engaged on a contractual basis as advisers and trainers to the Russians.

Having survived a particularly difficult period during the 1980's, the principal casualty of which was the Velindre Works which closed in 1989, the Welsh Tinplate industry is once again able to compete successfully on product cost and quality terms with the best in the world and is well-prepared to meet the challenges of the twenty-first century, having survived those of the previous two centuries.

As for the old hand mills works, all but a few have already disappeared from view. Those that remain are being used for purposes far remote from their original function. Sadly, many of the old tinplaters, too, have now passed on, leaving those of us who remain to gratefully reflect on the impact they have made on our memories, our communities and our culture. We have Lord Glantawe to thank for the Mumbles Pier, Swansea, and Daniel Edwards for the magnificent Tabernacl Chapel in Morriston. In our national game we remember the immortal Albert Jenkins of Llanelli and the incorrigible Joe White of Morriston who played so sterlingly for Swansea R.F.C. In the fields of poetry and music the tinplate communities threw together the poet Daniel James ('Gwyrosydd' to use this bardic name), who worked for a short while at the Dyffryn Works, Morriston and John Hughes, who it is said, was at one time the Manager of the same works. Together they produced that most famous of Welsh hymns, 'Calon Lan'.

Emrys Jones, the founder conductor of the Manselton (near Swansea) Male Choir worked for many years in the trade at Morriston. It is his arrangement of 'Morte Christe' (When I Survey the Wondrous Cross) that is a particular favourite in the repertoire of many a male choir. In the field of visual arts, Ceri Richards, one of Wales' artists of international repute, was the son of a Gowerton tinplate worker. In the trade union movement, Sir Lincoln Evans, one-time General Secretary of the Iron and Steel Trades Confederation and two of his successors, Roy Evans and Keith Brookman, both began their union careers after having gained employment and experience in the trade. There are many others who, I am sure, are equally worthy of mention.

As a tribute to all those who laboured in the trade, the following 'folk poem' appropriately describes the regard that these men of steel had for their craft. Called 'Twenty by Fourteen or Twenty by Ten' (the standard dimensions in inches of tinplate sheets), it was penned anonymously.

He was an old Doubler and Ben was his name,
An old tinplate worker with no claim to fame,
Who wore wooden clogs and apron so white,
His life so enrapped in one great delight,
Which was twenty by fourteen or twenty by ten,
Nothing else mattered in the life of old Ben.

A pair of mill rolls was his life-long delight,
As he rolled his thick iron by day and day night,
And all that he knew from mountains to coasts,
Was that the Mill Superintendent was his Lord of Hosts,
Who else could be greater to him of all men,
In the world of his twenty by fourteen or twenty by ten.

235

With his week's work over and his rolls all down,
He'd call for an hour at the Welcome to Town,
And sip at his pint with a smoke now and then,
And listen—how empty were the topics of men,
No talk could be relished in a pub by Ben,
Without twenty by fourteen or twenty by ten.

So back to his mills on a Monday he'd plod,
And he'd smile at his rolls with a word and a nod,
To understand Ben his team never could,
But his rolls were his children and they understood,
By proud and dispute not these symbols of men,
By they twenty by fourteen or twenty by ten.

Memory still lingers but old Ben has passed on,
His last piece is doubled, the eights are all done;
As he lies in God's acre one length is his lot,
In a seventy by twenty it's now all that he's got,
But the Great Sorter will find in the mill work of Ben,
His prize of twenty by fourteen or twenty by ten.

The old mills are idle the last piece is rolled,
The matching is over each furnace is cold,
The Story is ended, the story of Ben,
And the glory that was twenty by fourteen, or twenty by ten.

Finally, and fittingly, I end with a quotation from Andrew Yarranton, without whose foresight there might never have been a Welsh Tinplate industry:

Reader it's possible, thou hast not all in this book that thou didst expect, and on the other hand, I tell thee, here is more than I intended.[14]

NOTES

[1] Tolliday, S.W., op. cit.
[2] British Steel plc Archives: *The Steel Company of Wales Limited.*
[3] Brooke, E.H., op. cit.
[4] British Steel plc., Archives.
[5] Ibid.
[6] Ibid.
[7] Ibid.
[8] British Steel plc., Archives.
[9] Wilkins, C., op. cit.
[10] Griffith, W.L. (The Canadian Government's Agent in Wales) Extract from his 1898 report quoted in Bennett, C. *The Welsh in Canada* (Juniper Books Ltd., Renfrew, Ontario, 1985).
[11] Rutherford, R., op. cit.
[12] Conway, R., (Ed), op. cit.
[13] Griffiths, T., *Report following visit to Moscow Metal Works* (1913).
[14] Yarranton, A., op. cit.

Tinplate workers, Cwmfelin Works, Swansea, *c.* 1910.

238

BIBLIOGRAPHY

The information contained in this book has been drawn from many sources. Of significance are the following:

1. **Manuscript Sources**
   British Steel plc Archives
   Cardiff City Library (Melingriffith MSS 1853-7 and Conway MSS relating to Pontrhydyrun Works 1831-68).
   Glamorgan County Records Office
   National Library of Wales (Tregonning MSS relating to Morfa Works Llanelli).
   National Science Museum (Rhys Jenkins Collection).
   The Iron and Steel Trades Confederation Archives
   University College, Swansea Archives
   West Glamorgan County Records Office
   In addition, much use has been made of documents obtained to the author in researching the tinplate industry in Wales.

2. **Official Publications**
   Report of the Commissioners on the Employment of Children in factories, 1833
   Report of the Royal Commission on Education in Wales 1847
   Report of the Commissioners on the Truck Acts 1871 and 1872
   Annual Report of Trade Unions by the Chief Labour Correspondent
   Annual Report on Changes in Rates of Wages and Hours of Labour in the United Kingdom 1894-1901
   Report on Collective Agreement 1910
   Collis, E.L. and Hilditch, J., *Report on the Conditions of Employment in the Manufacture of Tinplates,* Cmd. 6394 (1912)
   Industrial Council: Minutes of Evidence taken before the Industrial Council in connection with their Enquiry into Industrial Agreements, Cmd. 6953 (1913)
   Commission of Inquiry into Industrial Unrest, Cmd. 8668 (1917)
   Vernon H.M., *Influence of Hours of Work and Ventilation on Output in Tinplate Manufacture,* Report of the Industrial Fatigue Board 1919
   Board of Trade, *An Industrial Survey of South Wales,* 1932
   Iron and Steel Industry: Reports by the B.I.S.F. and the Joint Iron Council to the Minister of Supply. Cmd 6811 (1946).

3. **Newspapers, Journals**
   The Cambrian, The Dragon, The Economist, The Engineer, Engineering,

Industrial World, Ingot News, Iron and Coal Trades Review, Iron and Steel, Journal of the Iron and Steel Institute, Ryland's Directory, The South Wales Evening Post. Also articles, features etc. contained in the publications of the South East Wales Industrial Archaeological Society, South West Wales Industrial Archaeology Society, The Swansea Valley History Society, The Port Talbot History Society, Neath Antiquarian Society and the Clydach History Society.

4. Unpublished Works (Thesis etc.)

The Social and Psychological effects of change in the Tinplate Industry of South West Wales. A study of the Hand Mill Works, J.K. Chadwick-Jones—PhD thesis, University College, Cardiff, 1960.

History of Tinplate Manufacturers in Llanelli, H. Hancocks—MA thesis University College, Swansea, 1965.

Economic Change in Industrial South Wales—Postwar Patterns and Developments, G. Humphreys, PhD Thesis, University College, Swansea, 1967.

'Historical Survey of the West Wales Steel Industry with Special reference to the Tinplate and Sheet Industries'. Treatise submitted by 'Poolpe' (a nom-de-plume) to the Royal National Eisteddfod of Wales, Llanelli. 1930.

5. Published Works

Boyns, T., Thomas, D., & Baber, C., 'The Iron, Steel & Tinplate Industries 1750-1914' in *Glamorgan County History,* Vol. I (Glamorgan County History Trust Ltd., 1980).

Barton, D.B., *A History of Tin Mining and Smelting in Cornwall,* (D. Bradford Barton Ltd., 1967).

Brooke, E.H., *Monograph on the Tinplate Works of Great Britain* (Swansea 1932); *Chronology of the Tinplate Works of Great Britain* (Cardiff 1942); 'Appendix' to the *Chronology of the Tinplate Works of Great Britain, 1665-1949* (Cardiff, 1949).

Burn, Duncan, *The Steel Industry 1939-1959* (Cambridge University Press, 1961).

Carr, J.C. & Taplin, W., *History of the British Steel Industry* (Basil Blackwell, Oxford, 1962).

Chappell, E.H. 'Historic Melingriffith'. Cardiff 1940.

Flower, P.W. 'A History of the Trade in Tin' London 1880.

Gibbs, F.W., "The Rise of the Tinplate Trade: I The Tinplate Workers; II Early Tinplate Manufacture; III John Hanbury; IV An Eighteenth Century Tinplate Mill, *Annals of Science,* Vol. V (1950), Vol. VI (1951).

Hatch, J., *English tin Production and Trade Before 1550* (Clarendon Press, Oxford, 1973).

Hawthorne, J.G. & Smith, C.S. *On Diverse Acts: The Treatise of Theophilus* (University of Chicago Press, 1963).

Hoare, W.E. 'Development of the Tinplate Industry in Great Britain', *The Institute of Metallurgists,* Volume III, No. 1 (March 1951).

Ince, Lawrence, 'Neath Abbey Iron Company', De Archaeologische Pers. 1984.

Jones, Sir Edgar R., *The Tinplate Industry* (London, 1914).

Leng, Philip J., *The Welsh Dockers* (G.W. & A. Hesketh, Ormskirk, 1981).

Manners, G. (Ed), *South Wales in the Sixties* (Pergamon Press, 1964).

Minchinton W., *The British Tinplate Industry: A History* (Oxford University Press, 1964).

Pride, E., *Tinman's Progress* (Swansea, 1959).

Pugh, Sir Arthur, *Men of Steel by One of Them* (Iron and Steel Trades Confederation, 1951).

Reader, W.J., *Metal Box: A History* (Heinemann, London, 1976).

Reaumur, R-A.F., *De Principes de l'art de faire le fer-blanc* (Historie de l'Academie Royale des Sciences, Paris, 1725).

Rutherford, R. 'Romancing in Tinplate' The Wean Engineering Company, Warren, Ohio, 1951.

Samuel, J.R., *A Short History of Tin and the Tinplate Trade* (Newport, 1924).

Smith, Anthony, *A History of Tinplate* (Tin International, 1977/78).

Thomas, H. Spence, 'The Tinplate Trade: Some Recent Developments', *Proceedings of the South Wales Institute of Engineers,* 1913.

Wainwright, David, *Men of Steel: The History of Richard Thomas and his Family* (Quiller Press, London, 1986).

Warren, Kenneth, *The British Iron and Steel Sheet Industry Since 1840* (G. Bell and Sons, London, 1970).

Wilkins, C., *History of the Iron, Steel and Tinplate Trades* (Merthyr Tydfil, 1903).

Williams, D, Trefor, *The Economic Development of Swansea and of the Swansea District to 1921* (Cardiff, 1940).

Yarranton, A., *England's Improvement by Sea and Land* (London, 1677).

APPENDIX 'A'

LIST OF TINPLATE WORKS IN SOUTH WALES INCLUDING GOUCESTERSHIRE

(Sources: Brooke, E. H., *Chronology of Tinplate Works of Great Britain* and documents in Author's Collection)

WORKS	LOCATION	Date Erected		Date of Closure	
Abbey	Tintern, Gwent	Feb.	1880		1901
Aber	Llansamlet, Swansea, West Glam	Sept.	1880	Feb.	1941
Aberavon	Port Talbot, West Glam	Sept.	1880	Feb.	1953
Abercarn	Abercarn, Gwent		1875	May	1961
Aberdulais	Neath, West Glam		1830	July	1938
Aberlash (Tirydail)	Ammanford, Dyfed	Dec.	1889	June	1908
Abertillery	Abertillery, Dyfed		1846	Nov.	1957
Amman	Brynamman, Dyfed		1872		1897
Amman (Garnant)	Garnant, Dyfed	June	1881	June	1930
Anglo-Welsh (see Ynyscedwyn)	Ystradgynlais, Powys				
Ashburnham	Burry Port, Dyfed	April	1890	Feb.	1953
Avondale	Pontnewydd, Gwent		1877	Jan.	1958
Avon Vale	Port Talbot, West Glam		1866		1895
Baglan Bay	Briton Ferry, West Glam	Dec.	1889	Dec.	1956
Beaufort	Morriston, Swansea		1860		1942
Blaina	Blaina, Gwent	Nov.	1879	May	1905
Bryn	Ynysmeudw, Pontardawe, West Glam		1879	Jan.	1941
Brynmawr	Brynmawr, Gwent		1867		1871
Burry	Llanelli, Dyfed		1875	Jan.	1961
Burry Extension (Burry Box)	Llanelli, Dyfed		1912	May	1941
Byass (Mansel)	Port Talbot, West Glam		1822		1954
Caerleon	Caerleon, Gwent	1750-1760		Feb.	1941
Cambria	Pontardulais, West Glam		1874	Jan.	1938
Caldicott	Caldicott, Gwent	Feb.	1879	April	1896
Cardonnel	Skewen, West Glam	Feb.	1890	Dec.	1940
Carmarthen	Carmarthen, Dyfed		1760	Nov.	1899
Cilfrew	Neath, West Glam	Aug.	1878		1930
Clayton	Pontardulais, West Glam		1875	Nov.	1957
Clyne (see Resolven)	Resolven, Nr. Neath, West Glam				
Copper Mines'	Cwmafan, Port Talbot, West Glam		1825	June	1942
Cwmbwrla	Swansea, West Glam		1863	July	1929
Cwmfelin	Swansea, West Glam		1858	Mar.	1948
Cynon	Aberdare, Mid Glam		1868	Mar.	1946
Dafen	Llanelli, Dyfed		1846		c.1930
Dowlais	Merthyr Tydfil, Mid Glam	Nov.	1879		1883

WORKS	LOCATION	Date Erected		Date of Closure	
Dyffryn	Morriston, West Glam		1874	Jan.	1953
Dulais	Pontardulais, West Glam	May	1910	Mar.	1946
Dynevor	Pantyffynon, Nr. Ammanford, Dyfed	Oct.	1880	Mar.	1946
Ebbw Vale	Ebbw Vale, Gwent		1935	Continuing	
Edlogan	Pontrhydyrun, Gwent		1807	Mar.	1946
Elba	Swansea, West Glam	Feb.	1925	April	1953
Ely	Llantrisant, Mid Glam		1874	Mar.	1946
Fairwood	Gowerton, West Glam	April	1886	Mar.	1946
Ferry (Vernon)	Briton Ferry, West Glam		1850	Mar.	1946
Ffrwdwyllt	Port Talbot, West Glam	Aug.	1881	Feb.	1953
Garnant (see Amman)	Garnant, Dyfed				
Gilwern	Gilwern, Nr Abergavenny, Gwent		1813		1884
Gilwern (see Phoenix)	Clydach, West Glam				
Glamorgan	Pontardulais, West Glam		1872	Dec.	1961
Glanrhyd	Pontardawe, West Glam	May	1879	Jan.	1953
Glantawe (see Glanrhyd)	Pontardawe, West Glam				
Glanyrafon (see Park)					
Glynbeudy	Brynamman, Dyfed	Mar.	1880		1942
Glynhir	Pontardulais, West Glam	Oct.	1910	Dec.	1961
Gorseinon	Gorseinon, West Glam		1881	April	1957
Gower	Penclawdd, West Glam		1872	Mar.	1895
Grovesend	Gorseinon, West Glam		1886	Mar.	1953
Gwalia	Briton Ferry, West Glam	Nov.	1892	June	1953
Gyrnos	Lower Cwmtwrch, West Glam		1876	Mar.	1946
Hendy	Hendy, Dyfed		1866		1953
Jersey (see Wern)	Briton Ferry, West Glam				
Kidweli	Kidweli, Dyfed		1719	Mar.	1946
King's Dock	Swansea, West Glam		1909	June	1957
Landore	Swansea, West Glam		1851		1901
Lion	Nantyglo, Gwent	Aug.	1880		1902
Llangennech	Llangennech, Dyfed		1867		1934
Llwydarth	Nr. Maesteg, Mid Glam		1868	Aug.	1900
Lower Pontnewydd	Pontnewydd, Gwent		1802	June	1885
Lydbrook	Lydbrook, Glos.		1706		1925
Lydney	Lydney, Glos.		1818	Nov.	1957
Mansel (see Byass)	Port Talbot, West Glam				
Mardy	Gorseinon, West Glam	Mar.	1910	Oct.	1957
Melingriffith	Whitchurch, Nr. Cardiff		c.1910	Oct.	1957
Melyn	Neath, West Glam	July	1864	Dec.	1946
Monmouth	Monmouth, Gwent		1869		1886
Morfa	Llanelli, Dyfed		1851	Aug.	1942
Morlais	Llangennech, Dyfed		1863	Mar.	1946
Morriston & Midland	Morriston, West Glam		1872	May	1952

WORKS	LOCATION	Date Erected	Date of Closure
Neath Abbey	Neath, West Glam	c.1885	c. 1895
Old Castle	Llanelli, Dyfed	1886	July 1957
Old Lodge	Llanelli, Dyfed	Jan. 1880	Mar. 1946
Park (Glanyrafon)	Clydach, West Glam	Dec. 1879	Mar. 1946
Parkend	Lydney, Glos.	1853	1881
Pemberton	Llanelli, Dyfed	Jan. 1911	Nov. 1957
Pencoed	Bynea, Nr. Llanelli, Dyfed	Aug. 1928	Mar. 1946
Pentyrch	Taffs Well, Mid Glam	Mar. 1890	1931
Penygored	Llechryd, Dyfed	c.1765	c.1813
Phoenix (Gilwern)	Lower Cwmtwrch, West Glam	Oct. 1869	Mar. 1946
Player's	Clydach, West Glam	c.1880	April 1958
Pontardawe (Gilbertson's)	Pontardawe, West Glam	1835	1957
Ponthir	Caerleon, Gwent	1747	c.1915
Pontymister	Pontymister, Gwent	1843	Mar. 1946
Pontypool	Pontypool, Gwent	1720	June 1957
Raven	Glanamman, Dyfed	1881	1940
Redbrook	Pontnewydd, Gwent	1771	c.1940
Resolven (Clyne)	Resolven, West Glam	1879	Mar. 1946
Rhiwderin	Rhiwderin, Nr. Newport, Gwent	1867	1886
R. T. Mills	Llanelli, Dyfed	1910	Sept. 1954
St. Davids (Yspitty)	Loughor, Dyfed	1869	Dec. 1957
South Wales	Llanelli, Dyfed	1872	Jan. 1941
Teilo	Pontardulais, West Glam	Jan. 1880	Oct. 1957
Tirydail (see Aberlash)			
Treforest	Treforest, Mid Glam	1794	Aug. 1946
Trevor	Pontypool, Gwent	1888	1892
Trostre	Llanelli, Dyfed	1951	Continuing
Tyde	Rogerstone, Gwent	c.1790	1881
Upper Forest & Worcester	Morriston, West Glam	1845	Mar. 1958
Velindre	Llangyfelach, West Glam	1956	Sept. 1989
Victoria (see Villiers)	Briton Ferry, West Glam		
Villiers (Victoria)	Briton Ferry, West Glam	Oct. 1888	Jan. 1953
Waterloo	Machen, Gwent	1826	Jan. 1941
Wern (Jersey)	Briton Ferry, West Glam	1890	Mar. 1946
Western	Llanelli, Dyfed	1863	Jan. 1953
Ynyscedwyn (Anglo-Welsh)	Ystradgynlais, Powys	June 1889	Aug. 1941
Ynyspenllwch	Glais, Nr. Clydach, West Glam	c.1745	1897
Ynysygerwn	Nr. Neath, West Glam	c.1753	1835
Yspitty (St. Davids)	Loughor, Dyfed	1869	1957
Ystalyfera	Ystalyfera, Powys	c.1846	Mar. 1946

APPENDIX 'B'

NUMBERS EMPLOYED IN SOUTH WALES TINPLATE INDUSTRY
('OLD TYPE' WORKS ONLY)

Sources: Brooke, E. H., *Chronology of Tinplate Works of Great Britain*; Minchinton, W., *The British Tinplate Industry: A History* and documents in Author's Collection)

Year	Male	Female	Total
1800	—	—	1,000
1834	—	—	4,000
1851	—	—	5,200
1871	—	—	9,200
1880	—	—	15,500
1891	—	—	25,000
1898	—	—	16,000
1901	12,048	2,967	15,015
1906	—	—	20,000
1909	—	—	23,550
1911	20,180	2,802	22,982
1913	—	—	28,500
1918	—	—	15,100
1923	24,580	4,320	29,900
1928	28,230	3,810	32,040
1930	27,900	3,720	31,620
1939	24,160	2,510	26,670
1944	—	—	10,797
1949	15,530	2,810	18,340
1954	12,160	2,070	14,230
1959	—	—	2,880
1964	—	—	1,500

APPENDIX 'C' (1)

TINPLATE TRADE

STATEMENT SHOWING TIME TOTAL NUMBER OF EMPLOYEES ON PAY ROLL

February 1939 and July 1941 (Sources : British Steel plc Archives)

REF. NO.	AREA AND WORKS THEREIN	NUMBER OF PERSONS EMPLOYED													
		AT FEBRUARY 1939							AT JULY 1941						
		MEN			WOMEN			TOTAL	MEN			WOMEN			TOTAL
		OVER 18	UNDER 18	TOTAL	OVER 18	UNDER 18	TOTAL		OVER 18	UNDER 18	TOTAL	OVER 18	UNDER 18	TOTAL	
A.	**LLANELLY & WEST OF LLANELLY AREA:**														
	ASBURNHAM														
	KIDWELLY														
	MORLAIS														
	OLD CASTLE														
	OLD LODGE														
	PEMBERTON	3,856	281	4,137	361	177	538	4,675	1,636	232	1,868	211	101	312	2,180
	BURRY														
	SOUTH WALES														
	R. T. MILLS														
	MOREA														
	PENCOED														
	WESTERN														
B.	**PONTARDULAIS, AMMANFORD AND LOUGHOR AREA:**														
	DULAIS														
	GLYNHIR														
	CAMBRIA														
	AMMAN														
	HENDY	2,092	149	2,241	195	81	276	2,517	1,601	196	1,787	202	81	283	2080
	DYNEVOR														
	ST. DAVID'S														
	TEILO														
	CLAYTON														
	GLYNBEUDY														
	GLAMORGAN														

APPENDIX 'C' (2)

REF. NO.	AREA AND WORKS THEREIN	NUMBER OF PERSONS EMPLOYED													
		AT FEBRUARY 1939							AT JULY 1941						
		MEN			WOMEN			TOTAL	MEN			WOMEN			TOTAL
		OVER 18	UNDER 18	TOTAL	OVER 18	UNDER 18	TOTAL		OVER 18	UNDER 18	TOTAL	OVER 18	UNDER 18	TOTAL	
C.	GORSEINON & GOWERTON AREA:														
	GOWERTON ⎫ FAIRWOOD ⎪ GROVESEND ⎬ GORSEINON ⎪ MARDY ⎭	1,437	125	1,562	117	14	131	1,693	710	121	831	104	35	139	970
D.	SWANSEA & DISTRICT AREA:														
	KING'S DOCK ⎫ BEAUFORT ⎪ MORRISTON ⎪ DYFFRYN ⎪ ABER ⎬ CWMBWRLA ⎪ CWMFELIN ⎪ UPPER FOREST ⎪ ELBA ⎭	4,189	346	4,535	359	125	484	5,019	2,290	373	2,653	264	144	408	3,061
E.	SWANSEA VALLEY AREA:														
	GYRNOS ⎫ PLAYER ⎪ PARK ⎪ BRYN ⎪ GILBERTSON ⎬ GLANRHYD ⎪ PHOENIX ⎪ ANGLO-WELSH ⎪ YSTALYFERA ⎭	1,629	203	1,832	172	32	204	2,036	580	113	693	67	31	96	791

APPENDIX 'C' (3)

NUMBER OF PERSONS EMPLOYED

REF. NO.	AREA AND WORKS THEREIN	AT FEBRUARY 1939							AT JULY 1941						
		MEN			WOMEN			TOTAL	MEN			WOMEN			TOTAL
		OVER 18	UNDER 18	TOTAL	OVER 18	UNDER 18	TOTAL		OVER 18	UNDER 18	TOTAL	OVER 18	UNDER 18	TOTAL	
F.	NEATH, NEATH VALLEY, BRITON FERRY & PORT TALBOT AREA: BAGLAN BAY, WERN, ABERAVON, FERRY, FFRWDWYLLT, GWALIA, MELYN, RESOLVEN, VILLIERS, VIVIAN, BYASS, COPPER MINERS, D.R. DAVIES, ABERDULAIS, CARDONNEL, CYNON, EAGLESBUSH	3,952	431	4,383	418	113	531	4,914	2,537	498	3,035	314	191	505	3,540
G.	EASTERN AREA: AVONDALE, ABERTILLERY, CAERLEON, CENTRAL, PONTYPOOL, PONTYMISTER, WATERLOO, OSBORNE, TYNEWYDD, ABERCARN, ELY, EDLOGAN, LYDNEY, MELINGRIFFITH, TREFOREST	3,111	363	3,474	168	27	195	3,669	1,521	269	1,786	80	26	106	1,892
H.	EBBW VALE								280	140					420
	TOTAL	20,266	1,898	22,164	1,790	569	2.36	24,523	11,145	1,942	12,663	1,242	609	1,851	14,934

250

APPENDIX 'D' (1)

NUMBERS EMPLOYED IN THE OLD HAND MILLS TINPLATE PLANTS

March 1946 to December 1957 (Source : British Steel plc Archives)

CLASSIFICATION OF OPERATIVES	NUMBERS AT																	
	FEB. 1946	FEB. 1947	FEB. 1948	FEB. 1949	FEB. 1950	FEB. 1951	FEB. 1952	DEC. 1952	JUNE 1953	DEC. 1953	JUNE 1954	DEC. 1954	JUNE 1955	DEC. 1955	JUNE 1956	DEC. 1956	JUNE 1957	DEC. 1957
A. MILLS																		
1. BAR CUTTERS	131	155	157	159	163	164	155	157	85	92	89	88	88	86	86	87	62	19
2. ROLLERMAN	470	667	698	729	719	710	663	663	378	412	392	384	387	381	378	347	235	75
3. DOUBLERS	511	698	710	734	735	727	700	657	393	427	415	410	394	403	395	390	249	82
4. FURNACEMEN	530	665	689	721	717	705	668	635	390	412	392	384	378	369	363	341	227	76
5. 1ST HELPERS	472	706	709	738	705	696	648	616	372	399	401	376	383	383	406	401	258	75
6. 2ND HELPERS	467	723	677	771	740	710	683	650	361	416	404	388	376	380	388	383	243	76
7. BEHINDERS	451	985	1068	795	807	811	776	772	389	392	420	421	425	488	459	454	263	75
8. TRAINEES BRITISH	-	-	(incl in 7)	108	82	62	37	27	12	17	9	19	7	7	8	6	4	-
OTHER FOREIGN WKRS	-	-		139	125	14	6	4	-	1	-	-	-	-	-	-	1	2
ITALIANS	-	-	-	-	-	76	61	20	-	69	12	9	27	59	95	64	18	7
9. SHEARERS	177	225	232	230	243	243	228	220	128	137	136	134	134	130	128	122	85	29
10. BUNDLERS	290	367	355	384	376	360	364	351	185	207	205	204	202	205	207	189	133	56
11. OPENERS: EXPERIENCED	545	772	764	772	770	787	785	741	433	445	438	433	435	416	414	396	270	87
LEARNERS	-	-	-	53	52	59	39	28	11	13	13	16	17	13	14	16	11	2
12. BLACKPLATE WHEELERS	42	46	48	66	52	54	54	52	30	31	31	32	28	30	31	31	23	7
13. BLACKPLATE WEIGHERS	37	43	50	48	50	47	50	45	31	31	28	30	30	31	31	30	16	7
14. ALL OTHER MILL LABOUR	303	463	465	455	500	523	501	527	292	308	290	305	284	290	298	268	214	90
TOTAL	4426	6515	6622	6910	6836	6748	6408	6135	3490	3809	3675	3633	3595	3671	3701	3525	2312	765
(B) INTERMEDIATE DEPARTMENTS																		
1. PICKLING	376	468	459	422	415	434	432	457	279	303	289	284	264	262	259	270	232	104
2. ANNEALING	392	495	534	541	542	535	516	495	317	339	319	320	314	312	287	299	241	72
3. COLD ROLLS	1232	1602	1444	1523	1500	1502	1617	1580	800	922	915	901	896	854	890	832	649	194
TOTAL	2000	2565	2437	2486	2457	2471	2565	2532	1396	1564	1523	1505	1474	1428	1436	1401	1122	370

APPENDIX 'D' (2)

NUMBERS EMPLOYED IN THE OLD HAND MILLS TINPLATE PLANTS

March 1946 to December 1957 (Source : British Steel plc Archives)

CLASSIFICATION OF OPERATIVES	FEB. 1946	FEB. 1947	FEB. 1948	FEB. 1949	FEB. 1950	FEB. 1951	FEB. 1952	DEC. 1952	JUNE 1953	DEC. 1953	JUNE 1954	DEC. 1954	JUNE 1955	DEC. 1955	JUNE 1956	DEC. 1956	JUNE 1957	DEC. 1957
(C) FINISHING DEPARTMENT																		
1. TINMEN	341	502	543	542	544	538	558	600	401	402	371	359	349	345	340	361	347	144
2. ATTENDERS	150	236	238	259	252	255	265	301	201	191	175	157	150	168	169	188	172	76
3. SANDERS	31	30	49	34	34	34	42	52	48	53	55	50	50	49	54	62	64	53
4. WIPERS & RISERS	48	26	24	24	19	22	18	12	16	22	12	22	22	21	16	16	11	3
5. DUSTERS	198	345	323	280	296	331	308	359	216	245	238	178	154	163	175	169	167	48
6. SPLITTING MACHINE OPERS.	116	154	162	288	183	174	182	208	134	135	127	120	119	115	110	116	120	58
7. RECKONERS	150	224	238	228	228	232	241	257	185	186	176	169	164	160	161	218	210	127
8. ASSORTERS	161	192	205	192	203	199	193	208	159	153	144	136	135	137	134	145	136	77
9. PACKERS	76	85	82	80	87	86	86	85	75	68	66	63	59	62	61	59	56	23
10. SHIPPERS	459	572	558	563	587	527	546	567	413	431	438	507	509	518	526	583	535	261
11. OTHER TINHOUSE LABOUR																		
TOTAL	1814	2486	2549	2462	2531	2508	2550	2782	1929	1949	1871	1821	1774	1810	1819	2005	1889	938
(D) OTHER LABOUR																		
1. GANTRY DRIVERS	118	142	149	147	150	147	154	156	114	122	117	116	114	115	111	117	104	47
2. ENGINE DRIVERS	128	152	164	165	158	163	160	161	103	102	96	96	92	89	86	79	66	35
3. BOILER FIREMEN	136	178	182	183	176	174	175	169	108	198	99	96	94	95	96	92	88	42
4. LOCO DRIVERS & SHUNTERS	48	47	50	50	50	49	49	50	40	36	35	36	36	35	35	35	33	22
5. FITTERS, MILLWRIGHTS, SMITHS ELECTRICIANS ETC.	349	391	444	449	470	466	473	446	378	368	363	354	359	368	380	394	324	215
6. FITTERS LABOURERS, MILLWRIGHTS ASSISTANTS, SMITHS STRIKERS ETC.	238	266	309	344	345	361	387	382	283	289	250	261	264	265	274	290	336	176
7. APPRENTICES	40	40	50	63	69	70	77	79	61	62	60	58	61	56	56	52	48	27
8. ALL OTHER LABOUR NOT INCLUDED IN ABOVE	981	1087	889	804	717	732	720	672	520	522	482	353	373	365	365	400	315	251
TOTAL	2038	3403	2237	2205	2135	2162	2195	2115	1607	1609	1502	1370	1393	1388	1403	1459	1314	815

APPENDIX 'D' (3)

NUMBERS EMPLOYED IN THE OLD HAND MILLS TINPLATE PLANTS

March 1946 to December 1957 (Source : British Steel plc Archives)

CLASSIFICATION OF OPERATIVES	NUMBERS AT																	
	FEB. 1946	FEB. 1947	FEB. 1948	FEB. 1949	FEB. 1950	FEB. 1951	FEB. 1952	DEC. 1952	JUNE 1953	DEC. 1953	JUNE 1954	DEC. 1954	JUNE 1955	DEC. 1955	JUNE 1956	DEC. 1956	JUNE 1957	DEC. 1957
SUMMARY																		
(A) MILLS	4426	6515	6622	6910	6836	6748	6408	6135	3490	3809	3675	3633	3595	3671	3701	3525	2312	765
(B) INTERMEDIATE	2000	2565	2437	2486	2457	2471	2565	2532	1396	1564	1523	1505	1474	1428	1436	1401	1122	370
(C) FINISHING	1814	2486	2549	2462	2531	2508	2550	2782	1929	1949	1871	1821	1774	1810	1819	2005	1889	938
(D) OTHER LABOUR	2038	2303	2237	2205	2135	2162	2195	2115	1607	1609	1502	1370	1393	1388	1403	1459	1314	815
TOTAL	10278	13869	13845	14063	13959	13889	13718	13564	8422	8931	8571	8329	8236	8297	8359	8390	6637	2888
MILLS IN OPERATION																		
ON 8-HOUR SHIFTS	114	54	83	111	112	112	126	129	47	65	63	62	62	69	62	69	52	6
ON 6-HOUR SHIFTS	26	125	105	94	86	86	65	50	52	48	48	47	47	38	43	26	23	17
TOTAL	140	179	188	205	198	198	191	179	99	113	111	109	109	107	105	95	75	23
AVERAGE OUTPUTS																		
BASIS BOXES	147500	190000	222500	238500	243000	251000	241000	220000	115000	140000	140000	138000	132800	122800	129700	116500	102000	44000

APPENDIX 'E'

REPORT OF TOM GRIFFITHS
OF THE STEEL SMELTERS UNION
ON VISIT TO MOSCOW, OCTOBER 1913

The journey to Moscow was very pleasant, but it was also tedious, on account of the confinement in the train for nights and days.

I was met on the station when I arrived at Moscow by Mr. Cound, the manager of the works, and a large number of Welshmen.

The weather was very cold, the winter having set in, and the people were making preparations for the snow and ice, which remains on the ground from October to March every year. While the snow and ice are on the ground, the people travel to and from their work on sledges. The Welsh tinplaters, however, have one advantage over the other people, because their houses are built within the walls of the works, therefore the time occupied in getting to the mills is only about three minutes from the house. The Welshmen are very well acclimatised, and they get into the beautiful city of Moscow on sleighs, in fur lined coats and caps and Wellington boots.

To watch the sun shining on the golden domes of the churches in this city is one of the finest sights in the world.

The Welshmen have got into the Russian method of living—up early in the morning to work and down late at night in all the places of amusement that are provided for the people. They earn good money, and some of them are saving for the rainy day: yet the men and their wives take part in all the sports and pastimes, such as football, tennis, hockey etc.

The city of Moscow is beautiful with its grand churches, monuments, big bells, and other great sights. It is like other great cities in the world, with its immense wealth on the one hand and great poverty on the other. The poorer classes in the city are apparently going through the same stages of progress as the working classes in our country went through 150 years ago.

The monasteries and the churches are very rich, and the poor people are provided with about 4,000 churches to worship in, but the houses that four or five families have to live in together are a disgrace to civilisation. Some of the sights I witnessed would shock even some of our slum dwellers.

Vodka, the chief drink in Russia, is a great curse. This spirit is a Government monopoly, from which a tremendous revenue is obtained, but it destroys the life and soul of all who consume it, and its effect may be seen among women and children in Russia. The standard of morals of the people appears to be low, and the condition of women and young girls in the factories is deplorable.

Wages are also very low in all the industries. One rouble a day (about two shillings and two pence of our money—11p) is considered a big wage for a man. One shilling a day (5p) is also considered a high wage for a woman. Practically all the women work in the factories, they are the slaves of the men. Some of the peasants in the agricultural districts earn about four pence (1½p) a day. They live on black bread, potatoes, and salt. Even in the suburbs of the city the people have to buy their water for drinking and washing purposes, and in the case of those who cannot afford to buy water the result can be better imagined than described. In fact, the poorer people live more like beasts than men, and you can imaging the moral state when you consider that there is an average of 40 new born babies picked up daily and taken to a foundling hospital, and that the children are buried from the same hospital at the rate of 30 per day.

The cruel laws under which the people live are accountable for several of these things; they live under oppression, tyranny, and serfdom. It is a great difficulty to get into Russia, but it is far more difficult to get out. I had to report myself to the Chief of the Police before I could sleep in Moscow, and I had to have a permit before I could leave the town again. The whole atmosphere was one of oppression and confinement, and one felt greatly relieved to breathe the atmosphere of freedom on British soil.

The educational system is very bad, only 25 per cent, of the children are educated. The education is not compulsory, and this accounts for the ignorance of the poorer classes. If education were made compulsory, the schools would be inadequate to accommodate the children. The children commence school at eight years of age.

Trade Unions are quite illegal, therefore there is no Trade Union organisation among the working classes. But they have their secret methods of combining, and it is marvellous how they can bring about organised movements to better their conditions under such despotic and tyrannical circumstances. Little groups meet in secret places, and the instructions are spread like wildfire through all the factories. The method of bringing about a stoppage of work is perfect, and the loyalty found among the men and women is splendid. It is the educated students who are really leading the working classes.

I witnessed a strike of tramwaymen while at Moscow, which paralysed the whole city, and it had not settled when I left the place. The leaders invited the workmen to the Forest for a meeting, but as soon as they had congregated together the soldiers were on the spot. Seventeen of the leaders were arrested, and hundreds of others were taken to prison. The drivers were paid 15s. (75p) per week, and the conductors about 13s. (65p) per week. They were asking for a 50 per cent advance, and after being idle for four days the demands of the men were granted. The cars commenced running on Saturday evening, but on Sunday it was reported that the seventeen leaders had been shot, and then the men came out again. The cars were then run by soldiers and the policemen, but the windows were all smashed, and the people were afraid to travel in the cars, and they all stopped running that evening. Fifteen thousand hands came out of the factories the following day in sympathy with the tramwaymen, and the authorities were afraid that a repetition of the revolution of 1905 was going to take place unless something was done.

I was in two or three of the secret houses with barred doors, and I left Moscow, leaving the strikers in the middle of the fight, wishing them God speed and every success.

In concluding these brief statements, I may say that there is a curious mixture in the Russians. They allow themselves to be ill-treated almost to death; they suffer everything, physically, socially, industrially, and spiritually. The quiet dignity of these poor, oppressed wretches is enough to astonish any civilised human being.

It seems as if the sinews of active strength were severed, as there are no signs of individual character, and no strength of will. The dictates of the Church, the power of the authorities, and the will of the Czar are everything to the Russian, for there is no consciousness of his own independence existing in his breast. They are victims of a long servitude, but if they keep marching onward there are hopes for a bright and noble future even for the Russians.

While the foregoing is somewhat outside the scope of my business in Russia, I thought that information on the social life of the Russian workers would be of interest to our members. The object of my visit was fully realised, and I received every help from Mr. Cound, the manager of the Moscow Metal Works, and also the workmen.

I have had a clear and open door to make my investigation. I was allowed in the works during the morning, afternoon, and night, so that I could see what was being done during the night as well as by day. The tinplate plant at Moscow is the very finest I have ever seen, and there is every credit due to Mr. Cound (an old pupil of Mr. Harrop, of Gorseinon) for designing and placing down such an excellent plant. Every facility is given the millmen to turn out work. Mr. Cound also realised that powerful machinery was not going to relieve the hard, physical work of the tinplater; he therefore introduced improved working conditions by placing extra men in the mill to relieve the tinplater of his physical work, and at the same time his earning power has been increased.

TERMS USED IN THE TINPLATE TRADE

ANNEALING—Controlled heating and subsequent cooling of steel to remove stresses introduced during the rolling process thereby improving the cold working properties of the steel. In tinplate processing by the Hand Mill method there were two annealing stages, i.e., Black Annealing after Hot Rolling and White Annealing after Cold Rolling.

ASSORTING—Process by which tinned sheets were examined individually by experienced tinplaters for the purpose of identifying any with defects and 'sorting' them into groups of Primes, Menders, Wasters, Waste Waste and scrap.

BASIS BOX—Until 1st January 1964, the standard unit of quantity for the production and sale of tinplate. It denoted the area of 31,360 square inches covered by 112 tinplate sheets each 20" by 14" inches in dimension or 224 sheets each 14" by 10". It was replaced in 1964 by the 'Standard Area of Tinplate' (SAT), based on 100,000 square inches in multiples of 100 sheets instead of 112 sheets or multiples thereof under the Basis Box arrangement. The SAT is now metricated and known as SITA (Standard International Tinplate Area). The Basis Box had a standard weight (or substances) of 108 lbs. (See schedule at the foot of this section).

BEHINDER—In Welsh Tinplate and Sheet Mills, the man who stood behind the Hot Mill and caught the bar or sheet (with the aid of a pair of tongs) as it emerged from the mill and passed it back over the top roll of the mill to the Rollerman. Before the introduction of the First Helper and the Second Helper into the mill crew, the Behinder was the lowest grade in the crew. Ahead of him, in sequential order from the top, was the Rollerman, Furnaceman and Doubler.

BESSEMER STEEL—Steel made by the process developed by Henry Bessemer. It involved blowing air through molten iron placed in a 'converter' —a pear shaped iron or steel plated and refractory lined vessel. The oxygen in the air oxidised the carbon, silicon and manganese in the iron. The process could be acid (for low phosphorus irons) or basic (for high phosphorus irons).

BLACKPLATE—Iron or, as later, steel sheet rolled, pickled and annealed but not coated, e.g. with tin.

BOSH—A water tank adjacent to each tinplate Hot Mill by which the mill men cooled their tongs, etc.

BUNDLERS—Male juveniles in the old-style tinplate works. Their job usually involved collecting all scrap off-cuts and 'bundling' them up for return to the steelworks.

CHAFERY—A small hearth, fired on charcoal, coal or coke, used for re-heating wrought iron prior to re-working.

CHARCOAL TINPLATE—Originally, tinplate made from charcoal iron to distinguish it from coke tinplate, made from iron smelted in a furnace in which coke was used as the fuel. The term 'charcoal tinplate' continued in use even after charcoal was no longer used in the iron smelting process. It signified a higher quality plate (because of heavier tin coatings) than found in 'coke tinplate'. Even charcoal tinplate was subdivided into 'Common Charcoal' and the higher-graded (by tin coating weight) 'Charcoal'.

COKE TINPLATE—Ordinary coated tinplate for common applications and of a generally lower quality than 'charcoal tinplate'. 'Best Coke tinplate' was a grade between 'Coke' and 'Common Charcoal' tinplate.

COLD ROLLING—Any rolling mill in which the iron or steel is passed unheated through a rolling mill.

CROCODILE SHEAR—A mechanical shear with two blades pivoted together, one moving and one stationary. Used in the tinplate trade for cutting sheets to required sizes. The shears also incorporated a 'squeezer' fixed to the moving blade which opened and closed and which the Doubler used to complete the 'doubling' or folding of tinplate sheets into a 'pack'.

DEEP DRAWING STEEL—Low carbon steel destined for deep pressing (drawing).

DOUBLER—One of the, originally, four men comprising a tinplate Hot Mill crew. His job was to 'double' or fold the tinplate sheets during the hot rolling process and shear them to produce 2 packs of 8 sheets from a single iron or steel bar.

DOUBLE MILL—A matching pair of Hot Mills and Furnaces—one set for the roughing stage (primary rolling) and the other for the finishing stage (secondary rolling).

ELECTROLYTIC TINNING—The modern method of tinning blackplate by means of electro-deposition. Blackplate, in strip form, is passed through a solution which acts as an electrolyte by which tin, in solid anodes immersed in the solution, passes through the solution to adhere to the surface of the steel strip, acting as a cathode as a consequence of the transfer of an electrical charge to the strip as it passes over rollers.

FINERY—A charcoal hearth used to make wrought iron by the direct reduction process (i.e., direct from the ore).

FLUX—Substance used to assist the adherence of molten tin to the iron/steel sheet. Originally palm oil but, from the 1880s onwards, zinc chloride was used.

FORGE—Buildings and machinery used for the conversion of pig iron into wrought iron and enclosing furnaces and hammers (water or, as later, steam driven).

FURNACEMAN—Second man in the tinplate crew behind the Rollerman and ahead of the Doubler. His task was to maintain the Roughing and Finishing Furnaces and keep the Rollerman supplied with bars/sheets at the required pace and temperature.

GREASE POT—A bath of molten palm oil or tallow (or a mixture of both) into which sheets were dipped after hand tinning to allow surplus tin to drain off.

HAND MILL—A rolling mill in which the iron or steel bar is manhandled in a sequence of passes through the rolls to reduce its thickness.

HOT ROLLING—Rolling process in which the iron or steel bar is heated before passage through the rolls.

HOT DIP TINNING—The process of applying a coating of tin to iron or steel sheets by dipping them individually into a bath of molten tin. This was the traditional method of producing tinplate prior to the introduction of electrolytic tinning in the 1930s.

JAPPANING—A process which involved the application of a very hard black varnish base coat, subsequently decorated (usually with oriental scenes), on flat surfaces such as tinplate. Further coats of varnish or lacquer were added to give a hard-wearing finish.

LACQUERED—Tinplate coated on one or both sides with a lacquer for extra protection or appearance.

LIST—Small bead of tin sometimes remaining on one edge of a sheet of tinplate processed by the Hot Dipped method. The bead was subsequently removed by dipping the edge of the sheet into a pot of molten tin (called the List Pot).

MENDERS—Sub-standard tinplates which could be rectified by a further coating of tin.

OPENERS—Female employees in the old hand mill plants whose job it was to prise apart, either manually or with the aid of a metal cleaver, sheets which had become stuck together during the rolling process.

PACK ROLLING—Rolling of sheets in packs (achieved by folding or 'doubling' the sheets several times) until the required thickness of each sheet is obtained. The 'Welsh' or 'Five Part' system involved five passes of a single bar through the furnaces and mills. The result was two packs each comprising eight sheets (i.e., 16 sheets in total).

PICKLING—Treating the surface of iron or sheet with a hot acid solution to remove scale (formed during the rolling processes), rust and dirt prior to further processing (cold rolling, tinning). As with Annealing, there were two stages of Pickling in the Hand Mill plants, i.e., Black Pickling and White Pickling.

PRIMES—Tinplates which achieve the highest quality standards.

RECKONING—The manual counting of tinned sheets into Boxes for subsequent packing prior to despatch.

ROLLERMAN—Principal job in the old style hand mills. It was the Rollerman's job to set the pace of work for the mill crew and to ensure good quality plates of the required dimensions were produced.

ROUGHING MILL—A rolling mill used for preliminary rolling (see DOUBLE MILL).

SCRUFF—An iron and tin compound which formed in the tin pot during the Hot Dip Tinning process. Removal of the scruff was necessary from time-to-time to prevent the pot from seizing up.

SIEMENS OPEN-HEARTH STEEL—Steel made by the Open-Hearth method developed by Sir William Siemens and used extensively for the manufacture of tinplate.

STICKERS—Hot pack-rolled sheets which have stuck together during rolling and have to be parted by hand.

SUBSTANCE—The thickness of tinplate expressed as weight per unit area (i.e., pounds per Basis Box originally). Common substance, denoted by the symbol, IC was 108 lbs. per Basis Box. IX = 136 lbs. per Basis Box. Each additional X after the first denoted an increase of 20 lbs. per B.B. over 136 lbs. Thus IXXX = 176 lbs. substance. Substances below IC (or common at 108 lbs.) were termed 'light' and denoted by the symbols ICL for 100 lbs. substance with an additional L added for each 5 lbs. below 100 lbs. Thus ICLLL would represent a substance of 90 lbs.

TAGGERS—Very thin tinplates.

TERNE PLATE—Thin iron or steel sheet, Hot Dip coated with a lead-tin compound (approx. 25% tin).

TIN (OR TINPLATE) BAR—Flat rolled steel bar, 15 to 20 foot in length by 9" in width with a thickness ranging from ⅜ inch to ⅞ inch.

TIN POT—Vessel containing molten tin into which iron or steel sheets were dipped for tinning. Tin pots could be single sweep (one pot of molten tin) or double sweep (with two separate pots working in tandem).

WASTERS—Tinplates containing defects which, unlike menders, usually were non-correctable. They were suitable for some specific applications and, because of the defects, were sold at a lower price than for prime tinplates.

WASTE WASTE—Defective tinplates below the standard of wasters but which nonetheless were suitable for some applications, and, of course, offered to customers at a lower selling price.

TINPLATE DENOMINATIONS AND SIZES ON THE BASIS BOX STANDARD

MARK	SIZE	SHEETS PER BOX	WEIGHT PER BOX	THICKNESS OF SHEETS	
	INS.		LBS.	MM	INS.
IC	14 x 10	225	108	0.313	0.0123
IX	"	"	136	0.395	0.0155
IXX	14 x 10	"	156	0.453	0.0179
IXXX	"	"	176	0.511	0.0201
IC	20 x 14	112	108	0.315	0.0123
ICLL	"	"	100	0.292	0.0114
ICLLL	"	"	95	0.277	0.0109
ICLLLL	"	"	90	0.262	0.0103
ICLLLLL	"	"	85	0.248	0.0097
ICL	"	"	80	0.233	0.0091
IX	"	"	136	0.396	0.0155
IXX	"	"	156	0.455	0.0179
IXXX	"	"	176	0.513	0.0201
IXXXX	"	"	196	0.571	0.0223
IC	28 x 20	"	216	0.315	0.0124
IX	"	"	272	0.396	0.0156
IC	"	56	108	0.315	0.0123
IX	"	"	136	0.396	0.0155
IC	20 x 10	225	154	0.313	0.0123
IX	"	"	194	0.394	0.0155
IC	14 x 18¾	124	110	0.309	0.0122
IC	14 x 19¼	120	110	0.311	0.0122
IC	30 x 21	112	243	0.315	0.0124
CL	"	"	224	0.290	0.0114
CLL	"	"	190	0.246	0.0097
CLLL	"	"	176	0.228	0.0090
CLLLL	"	"	160	0.207	0.0081
DC	17 x 12½	100	94	0.404	0.0160
DX	"	"	122	0.525	0.0206
DXX	"	"	143	0.615	0.0242
DXXX	"	"	· 164	0.706	0.0278
DXXXX	"	"	185	0.796	0.0313

INDEX

Unions
    The Dock Wharf, Riverside and General Workers' Union, later the Transport & General Workers Union, 191-4, 196
    National Amalgamated Association of Ironworkers, 185
    National Union of Gasworkers and General Labourers, 191, 192
    The Amalgamated Society of Engineers, 192
    The British Steel Smelters, Mill, Iron, Tinplate and Kindred Trades Association, later The Iron and Steel Trades Confederation, 191, 192, 196, 202, 205
    The Independent Association of Tinplate Workers, 177, 179, 184
    The South Wales, Monmouthshire and Gloucestershire Tinplate Workers Union, 186-91
    The Welsh Artisans Union, 192
    The Tin and Sheet Mill Men's Association, 191, 192, 196, 202

Warner, Richard (Revd), 112
Water power, 84
Watson (Bishop), 21
White, Joe, 235
Wierton Steel Company, 213
Williams, John Charles, 213
Williams, William, 210
Wilkins, Charles, 171, 232
Wills, Arthur, 38
Wright, Charles (Sir), 219, 228

Yarranton, Andrew, 19, 236

Zinc chloride flux, 157